LEAVING CERTIF

LESS STRESS MORE SUCCESS

Maths Revision
Ordinary Level
Paper 2

Brendan Guildea & Louise Boylan

g GILL EDUCATION

Gill Education

Hume Avenue

Park West

Dublin 12

www.gilleducation.ie

Gill Education is an imprint of M.H. Gill & Co.

© Brendan Guildea and Louise Boylan 2018

ISBN 978 07171 8318 0

Design by Liz White Designs
Artwork and print origination by MPS Limited

The paper used in this book is made from the wood pulp of managed forests.
For every tree felled, at least one tree is planted, thereby renewing natural resources.

At the time of going to press, all web addresses were active and contained information relevant to the topics in this book. Gill Education does not, however, accept responsibility for the content or views contained on these websites. Content, views and addresses may change beyond the publisher or author's control. Students should always be supervised when reviewing websites.

For permission to reproduce photographs, the authors and publisher gratefully acknowledge the following:

© Alamy: 128, 133, 228, 229; © Getty Images: 97; © russellstreet: 115;
© Shutterstock: 86, 93, 140, 143, 150; © Shutterstock/Michael Winston Rosa: 4.

The authors and publisher have made every effort to trace all copyright holders, but if any has been inadvertently overlooked we would be pleased to make the necessary arrangement at the first opportunity.

Acknowledgements

The authors would like to thank Carol Guildea and Joe Heron who helped with the proofreading, checked the answers and made many valuable suggestions that are included in the final text.

CONTENTS

Please note:
- The philosophy of your mathematics course is that topics can overlap, so you may encounter Paper 1 material on Paper 2 and vice versa.
- The exam questions marked by the symbol ⊙ in this book are selected from the following:
  1. SEC exam papers (relevant year indicated)
  2. Sample exam papers
  3. Original and sourced exam-type questions

Introduction

The aim of this revision book is to help you enhance your grade in your Leaving Certificate. The book is designed to be exam-focused. To do this, the book is based not just on the syllabus, but also on the examination paper. Because of this, this revision book can be used in conjunction with **any** textbook.

Throughout this book, **examples and exam-type questions are graded by level of difficulty**.

This level of difficulty is indicated by calculator symbols, as follows:

The number of calculators shown beside a question helps you know how difficult the question is. One calculator indicates a question which is relatively basic. As the questions get harder, the symbol will have more calculators. Three calculators indicates an average-level question, whereas five calculators indicates that it is a very challenging question. These questions may be beyond some students, but give them a go! **Students hoping to achieve a high grade should aim to complete all of the 'five calculator' questions.** The calculator symbol given for each question relates to the most difficult part of that question. **Don't be discouraged by a challenging question.** As in the Leaving Certificate exam, difficult questions can sometimes begin with one or two simple parts. You should attempt as much as you can.

It is very important to realise that **you are your own best teacher**. Revision is when you begin to teach yourself. Thus, it is very important for you to start your revision as soon as possible. Make notes while you are revising. If you are having difficulty with a particular question, seek help from your teacher, a friend or a member of your family. As with all subjects, the best examination preparation is to work through past examination or sample papers so that you are familiar with the layout and style of questions.

So let's start at the beginning. If you want to do well in your Leaving Certificate, then two things are essential:

- Revise effectively.
- Be familiar with the exam paper and so be prepared on the day of the exam.

These may seem obvious, but it's worth taking a moment to think about what these tips mean.

How to revise most effectively

If you are going to do well in the Leaving Certificate, you are going to spend quite a bit of time revising. Spending a little time learning how to revise effectively will help you get more from your time and will help you absorb and understand more of the material on the course. Here are some tips to help you revise for maths.

- Find a quiet place where you can work. This place should be dedicated to study and free of potential distractions. Turn off music, the TV, computer and mobile phone.

- Write a study plan. Don't be afraid to ask your parents/teachers/guidance counsellor for help at this stage.

- Do the more challenging revision first, when you are fresh. Trying to focus on difficult problems when you are tired can be counter-productive.

Study in small chunks of time lasting 25 to 35 minutes. Your memory and concentration will work better if you study in short frequent bursts.

- Maths is based on understanding, so while you can 'learn' some elements of the course, it is important that you develop an understanding of the material.

- Drill and practice are essential ingredients for success in maths.

- Try to link any new material to things you know already. This is learning through association and helps long-term retention.

Don't get hung up on more difficult material. Concentrate on understanding the fundamental concepts and being able to answer all straightforward questions. Then, with time, you can build up to the more challenging problems.

Leaving Certificate examination

Exam focus is critical to exam success. It is important to prepare yourself for the challenges you will face. By learning about the structure of the exam, you will learn how to maximise your points, allocate your time effectively and manage the paper without panic.

The order of the questions is not set and some questions may include cross-syllabus topics. The examination paper will be presented in two sections, as follows:

Section A – 150 marks
Concepts and Skills

Section B – 150 marks
Contexts and Applications

Read the exam paper right through at the start in order to determine which question is the easiest one to start with. Your mind may also be subconsciously processing some of the other problems.

Time yourself as follows

- Read the paper at the start: 5 minutes.
- Section A: 70 minutes.
- Section B: 70 minutes.
- Review your answers at the end: 5 minutes.
- Try to stick closely to these times. If you run out of time on a question, leave it and come back at the end.

Start with your best question, then your next best and so on. This way, if you are short of time, at least your best questions will be done.

Further exam tips

- There is no such thing as rough work in Maths – all work is relevant. If the examiner doesn't know how you reached an answer, even a correct answer, then full marks may not be awarded. Thus, **show all your work**.

Rule of thumb for timing yourself during the exam:

**Time spent on question =
½ (marks for question)**

That is, a 25-mark question should take no more than 12·5 minutes.

- Attempt marks (partial credit) will be awarded for any step in the right direction. Therefore, **make an attempt at each part of the question**. Even if you do not get the correct answer, you can still pick up most of the marks on offer if you show how you worked it out. Also, **draw a diagram where possible** because this can help you see the solution.

Attempt marks (partial credit) are valuable, so it is vital that you attempt all questions.
Leave **NO** blanks.

- If you cannot finish part of a question, leave a space and come back to it later. **Never scribble out any work or use Tipp-Ex.** Put a single line through it so that the examiner can still read it. In many cases, work that had a line through it received more marks. **Avoid using pencil** because the writing can be very faint and difficult to read.

- It is a good idea to show each stage of a calculation when using a calculator (in case you press a wrong key). Familiarise yourself with your calculator. Know your *booklet of formulae and tables* well and write down any formulae that you use.

Your calculator and *booklet of formulae and tables* are two extremely valuable resources to have in the exam. Make sure that you are very familiar with how your calculator works and that you know how to perform all functions on it. Also familiarise yourself with the *booklet of formulae and tables* so that you don't waste any time in the exam trying to find formulae.

Glossary of words used on the examination paper

Write down, state
You can write down your answer without showing any work. However, you can show some workings if you want to.

Calculate, find, show that, determine, prove
Obtain your answers by showing all relevant work. Marks are available for showing the steps leading to your final answer or conclusion.

Solve
Find the solution, or root, of an equation. The solution is the value of the variable that makes the left-hand side balance with the right-hand side.

Evaluate
Work out, or find, a numerical value by putting in numbers for letters.

Comment on
After studying the given information or answers, give your opinion on their significance.

Plot
Indicate the position of points on a graph, usually on the x- and y-planes.

Construct
Draw an accurate diagram, usually labelled, using a pencil, ruler, set square, compass and protractor. Leave all constructions on your diagram.

Sketch
Make a rough diagram or graph, labelled if needed.

Hence
You **must** use the answer, or result, from the previous part of the question.

Hence or otherwise
It is recommended that you use the answer, or result, from the previous part of the question, and it is usually best to do this, but other methods are acceptable.

Syllabus and checklist for Leaving Certificate Ordinary Level Maths Paper 2 exam

The philosophy your mathematics course is that topics can overlap, so you may encounter Paper 1 material on Paper 2 and vice versa.

The syllabus stresses that in all aspects of the Leaving Certificate Maths course, students should be able to:

- ☐ Explore patterns and formulate conjectures.
- ☐ Explain findings.
- ☐ Justify conclusions.
- ☐ Communicate mathematics verbally and in written form.
- ☐ Apply their knowledge and skills to solve problems in familiar and unfamiliar contexts.
- ☐ Analyse information presented verbally and translate it into mathematical form.
- ☐ Devise, select and use appropriate mathematical models, formulae or techniques to process information and to draw relevant conclusions.

Coordinate geometry of the line

- ☐ Use slopes to show that two lines are:
  - ○ parallel
  - ○ perpendicular.
- ☐ Recognise the fact that the relationship $ax + by + c = 0$ is linear.
- ☐ Solve problems involving slopes of lines.
- ☐ Calculate the area of a triangle.

Coordinate geometry of the circle

- ☐ Recognise that $(x - h)^2 + (y - k)^2 = r^2$ represents the relationship between the x and y coordinates of points on a circle centre (h, k) and radius r.
- ☐ Solve problems involving a line and a circle with centre $(0, 0)$.

Trigonometry

- ☐ Use the theorem of Pythagoras to solve problems.
- ☐ Define $\sin \theta$, $\cos \theta$ and $\tan \theta$ for all values of θ.
- ☐ Work with trigonometric ratios in surd form.

- [ ] Use trigonometry to calculate the area of a triangle.
- [ ] Solve problems using the sine and cosine rules (2D only).
- [ ] Solve problems involving the area of a sector of a circle and the length of an arc.

Geometry
Synthetic geometry

- [ ] Perform constructions 1, 2, 4, 5, 6 and 8–21.
- [ ] Use the following terms related to logic and deductive reasoning: theorem, proof, axiom, corollary, converse, implies.
- [ ] Investigate theorems 7, 8, 11, 12, 13, 16, 17, 18, 20, 21 and corollary 6 and use them to solve problems.

Transformation geometry, enlargements

- [ ] Investigate enlargements, paying attention to:
  - centre of enlargement
  - scale factor k, where $0 < k < 1, k \in \mathbb{Q}$
  - scale factor k, where $k > 1, k \in \mathbb{Q}$
  - area.
- [ ] Solve problems involving enlargements.

Length, area and volume

- [ ] Select and use suitable strategies to find:
  - the length of the perimeter and the area of the following plane figures: parallelogram, trapezium and figures made from combinations of these.
  - surface area and volume of the following solid figures: cylinder, right cone, right prism and sphere.
- [ ] Use the trapezoidal rule to approximate area.
- [ ] Investigate the nets of prisms (polygonal bases), cylinders and cones.
- [ ] Solve problems involving the length of the perimeter and the area of plane figures: disc, triangle, rectangle, square, parallelogram, trapezium, sectors of discs and figures made from combinations of these.
- [ ] Solve problems involving surface area and volume of the following solid figures: rectangular block, cylinder, right cone, triangular-based prism (right angle, isosceles and equilateral), sphere, hemisphere and solids made from combinations of these.

Probability
Counting

- [ ] List outcomes of an experiment.
- [ ] Apply the fundamental principles of counting.

- [ ] Count the arrangements of n distinct objects $(n!)$.
- [ ] Count the number of ways of arranging r objects from n distinct objects.

Concepts of probability

- [ ] Decide whether an everyday event is likely or unlikely to occur.
- [ ] Recognise that probability is a measure on a scale of $0-1$ of how likely an event is to occur.
- [ ] Use set theory; discuss experiments, outcomes, sample spaces.
- [ ] Use the language of probability to discuss events, including those with equally likely outcomes.
- [ ] Estimate probabilities from experimental data.
- [ ] Recognise that if an experiment is repeated, there will be different outcomes and that increasing the number of times an experiment is repeated generally leads to better estimates of probability.
- [ ] Associate the probability of an event with its long-run relative frequency.
- [ ] Discuss basic rules of probability (and/or, mutually exclusive) through the use of Venn diagrams.
- [ ] Calculate expected value and understand that this does not need to be one of the outcomes.
- [ ] Recognise the role of expected value in decision-making and explore the issue of fair games.

Outcomes of random processes

- [ ] Construct sample spaces for two independent events.
- [ ] Apply the principle that in the case of equally likely outcomes, the probability is given by the number of outcomes of interest divided by the total number of outcomes (examples using coins, dice, spinners, urns with coloured objects, playing cards, etc.).
- [ ] Find the probability that two independent events both occur.
- [ ] Apply an understanding of Bernoulli Trials.
- [ ] Solve problems involving up to three Bernoulli Trials.
- [ ] Calculate the probability that the first success occurs on the nth Bernoulli Trial where n is specified.

Statistics

Statistical reasoning with an aim of becoming a statistically-aware consumer

- [ ] Engage in discussions about the purpose of statistics and recognise misconceptions and misuses of statistics.
- [ ] Discuss populations and samples.

☐ Decide to what extent conclusions can be generalised.

☐ Work with different types of data (categorical, nominal or ordinal numerical, discrete or continuous) in order to clarify the problem at hand.

☐ Work with different types of bivariate data.

Finding, collecting and organising data

☐ Clarify the problem at hand.

☐ Formulate one (or more) questions that can be answered with data.

☐ Explore different ways of collecting data.

☐ Generate data or source data from other sources, including, the internet.

☐ Select a sample (simple random sample).

☐ Recognise the importance of representativeness so as to avoid biased samples.

☐ Discuss different types of studies: sample surveys, observational studies and designed experiments.

☐ Design a plan and collect data on the basis of the above knowledge.

Representing data graphically and numerically

Graphical:

☐ Describe the sample (both univariate and bivariate data) by selecting appropriate graphical or numerical methods.

☐ Evaluate the effectiveness of different displays in representing the findings of a statistical investigation conducted by others.

☐ Use stem and leaf plots and histograms (equal intervals) to display data.

☐ Explore the distribution of data, including concepts of symmetry and skewness.

☐ Compare data sets using appropriate displays, including back-to-back stem and leaf plots.

☐ Determine the relationship between variables using scatterplots.

☐ Recognise that correlation is a value from −1 to +1 and that it measures the extent of the linear relationship between two variables.

☐ Match correlation coefficient values to appropriate scatter plots.

☐ Understand that correlation does not imply causality.

Numerical:

☐ Use a variety of summary statistics to describe the data:
  ○ central tendency: mean, median, mode
  ○ variability: range.

☐ Recognise standard deviation and interquartile range as measures of variability.

☐ Use a calculator to calculate standard deviation.

☐ Find quartiles and the interquartile range.

☐ Use the interquartile range appropriately when analysing data.

☐ Recognise the existence of outliers.

Analysing, interpreting and drawing inferences from data

☐ Recognise how sampling variability influences the use of sample information to make statements about the population.

☐ Use appropriate tools to describe variability, drawing inferences about the population from the sample.

☐ Interpret the analysis.

☐ Relate the interpretation to the original question.

☐ Interpret a histogram in terms of the distribution of data.

☐ Make decisions based on the Empirical Rule.

1 Coordinate Geometry of the Line

☐ To know where to find the coordinate geometry formulae in the *booklet of formulae and tables*

☐ To learn how to apply these formulae to procedural and in-context examination questions

☐ To gain the ability, with practice, to recall and select the appropriate technique required by the exam questions

Coordinate geometry formulae

Six formulae for coordinate geometry are on page 18 of the *booklet of formulae and tables*. Here they are:

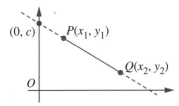

$$m = \frac{y_2 - y_1}{x_2 - x_1}$$ slope of PQ

$$|PQ| = \sqrt{(x_2 - x_1)^2 + (y_2 - y_1)^2}$$ length of $[PQ]$

$$\left(\frac{x_1 + x_2}{2}, \frac{y_1 + y_2}{2} \right)$$ midpoint of $[PQ]$

$$y - y_1 = m(x - x_1)$$
$$y = mx + c$$ equation of PQ

$$\frac{1}{2}|x_1 y_2 - x_2 y_1|$$ area of triangle OPQ

In addition, we must also know the following rules:

(i) Parallel lines have equal slopes.

If $l \| k \Leftrightarrow m_l = m_k$

(ii) If two lines are perpendicular then the product of their slopes equals -1.

If $l \perp k \Leftrightarrow (m_l)(m_k) = -1$

key point

m_l is the slope of l and m_k is the slope of k.

(iii) $y = 0$ is the equation of the x-axis.

$x = 0$ is the equation of the y-axis.

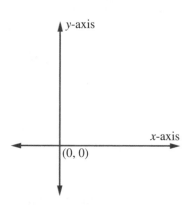

Rules (i), (ii) and (iii) are not in the *booklet of formulae and tables*. You have to know them!

Area of a triangle

The area of a triangle with vertices (corners) $(0, 0)$, (x_1, y_1) and (x_2, y_2) is given by the formula:

Area of triangle $= \frac{1}{2}|x_1y_2 - x_2y_1|$ (see *booklet of formulae and tables*, page 18)

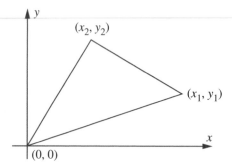

1. Always decide which point is (x_1, y_1) and which point is (x_2, y_2) before you use the formula.

2. The modulus symbol, $|\ |$, is included to make sure your answer is positive. This is because you cannot have a negative area. Therefore, if the above formula gives a negative answer, simply ignore the negative sign, e.g. $\frac{1}{2}|-10| = \frac{1}{2}(10) = 5$.

3. If none of the vertices is at the origin, simply select one of the vertices and map (move) it to the point $(0, 0)$ by a translation. Then apply the same translation to the other two vertices to get (x_1, y_1) and (x_2, y_2).

Example

(i) Plot the points $P(1, 5)$, $Q(-4, 2)$ and $R(3, -2)$ on a graph.

(ii) Find the area of the triangle PQR.

Solution

(i)

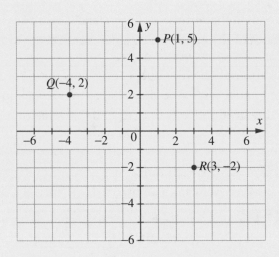

(ii) Map (move) the point $(1, 5)$ to $(0, 0)$.

Rule: Subtract 1 from x, subtract 5 from y.

$P(1, 5)$ $Q(-4, 2)$ $R(3, -2)$

$\downarrow$ $\downarrow$ $\downarrow$

$(0, 0)$ $(-5, -3)$ $(2, -7)$

          (x_1, y_1) (x_2, y_2)

$x_1 = -5, \ y_1 = -3, \ x_2 = 2, \ y_2 = -7$

Area of triangle

$= \frac{1}{2}|x_1 y_2 - x_2 y_1|$

$= \frac{1}{2}|(-5)(-7) - (2)(-3)|$

$= \frac{1}{2}|35 + 6|$

$= \frac{1}{2}|41|$

$= 20\frac{1}{2}$ square units

To find the area of a quadrilateral (four-sided figure), divide it into two triangles.

If the quadrilateral is a **parallelogram**, then the areas of both triangles are equal. Therefore, all that is needed is to find the area of one triangle and double it.

Intersecting lines

To find the point where two lines intersect, we solve the equations of the lines using the method of simultaneous equations, from algebra.

Simultaneous linear equations in two variables are solved with the following steps.

1. Write both equations in the form $ax + by = k$ and label the equations ① and ②.
2. Multiply one or both of the equations by a number in order to make the coefficients of x or y the same, but of opposite sign.
3. Add to remove the variable with equal coefficients but of opposite sign.
4. Solve the resultant equation to find the value of the remaining unknown (x or y).
5. Substitute this value in equation ① or ② to find the value of the other unknown.

Junior Cycle revision example

When geese fly in formation, they form an inverted V shape.

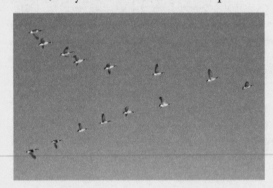

(i) If the lines of geese can be represented by the equations $2x + y - 11 = 0$ and $3x - 2y - 6 = 0$, find the coordinates of the leading goose.

(ii) After 1 hour, the leading goose has flown to a point $(37, 67)$.

Assuming the geese flew in a straight line and taking each unit to represent 1 km, find the distance travelled by the geese to the nearest km.

(iii) Hence, find the average flying speed in m/s.

Solution

(i) Solving the linear equations in two variables:

$$2x + y = 11 \qquad ①$$
$$3x - 2y = 6 \qquad ②$$
$$\overline{}$$
$$4x + 2y = 22 \qquad ① \times 2$$
$$3x - 2y = 6 \qquad ②$$
$$\overline{}$$
$$7x = 28 \qquad \text{(add)}$$
$$x = 4$$

Put $x = 4$ into ① or ②.

$$2x + y = 11 \qquad ①$$

$$2(4) + y = 11$$
$$8 + y = 11$$
$$y = 3$$

∴ The leading goose is at $(4, 3)$.

(ii) Use distance formula $= \sqrt{(x_2 - x_1)^2 + (y_2 - y_1)^2}$ (see *booklet of formulae and tables*, page 18)

Let $(x_1, y_1) = (4, 3)$ and $(x_2, y_2) = (37, 67)$

Distance $= \sqrt{(37 - 4)^2 + (67 - 3)^2} = \sqrt{1{,}089 + 4{,}096} = \sqrt{5{,}185}$
$= 72 \cdot 00694411$

Distance to nearest km $= 72$ km

(iii) Speed $= \dfrac{\text{Distance}}{\text{Time}} = \dfrac{72 \times 1{,}000}{60 \times 60} = 20$ m/sec

The exam may contain in-context questions at any stage. Be prepared to employ techniques learned elsewhere, as in the above question, where Speed $= \dfrac{\text{Distance}}{\text{Time}}$, which seems to have no link to coordinate geometry, yet it was required in this question.

Example

$A(8, 5)$ and $B(-10, 11)$ are two points. Find the midpoint of $[AB]$.

Solution

Midpoint formula $= \left(\dfrac{x_1 + x_2}{2}, \dfrac{y_1 + y_2}{2} \right)$ (see *booklet of formulae and tables*, page 18)

Let $(x_1, y_1) = (8, 5)$ and $(x_2, y_2) = (-10, 11)$

Midpoint $= \left(\dfrac{8 - 10}{2}, \dfrac{5 + 11}{2} \right) = \left(\dfrac{-2}{2}, \dfrac{16}{2} \right) = (-1, 8)$

In some questions we will be given the midpoint and one end point of a line segment and be asked to find the other end point.

To find the other end point, use the following method:

1. Make a rough diagram.
2. Find the translation that maps (moves) the given end point to the midpoint.
3. Apply the same translation to the midpoint to find the other end point.

Example

If $K(5, -3)$ is the midpoint of $[PQ]$ and $P = (4, 1)$, find the coordinates of Q.

Solution

1. Rough diagram

P(4, 1)　　　　　K(5, −3)　　　　　Q(?, ?)

2. Translation from P to K, $\overrightarrow{PK}$. Rule: Add 1 to x, take 4 from y.
3. Apply this translation to K:

$$K(5, -3) \longrightarrow (5 + 1, -3 - 4) = (6, -7)$$

∴ The coordinates of Q are $(6, -7)$.

Slope of a line

Slope of a line, m, given two points: $m = \dfrac{y_2 - y_1}{x_2 - x_1}$　(see *booklet of formulae and tables*, page 18)

Slope is $\dfrac{\text{Rise}}{\text{Run}} = \tan \theta$, where θ is the angle the line makes with the positive sense of the x-axis.

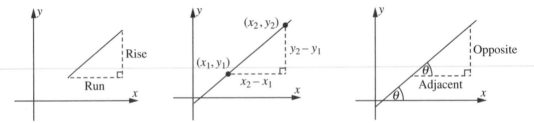

key point

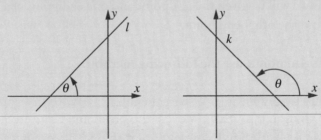

We say θ, the angle of inclination, is the angle formed between a line and the positive side of the x-axis.

The angle of inclination is always between 0° and 180°.

• It is always measured anticlockwise from the positive side of the x-axis.

- The line *l* has a positive slope where $0° < \theta < 90°$.   (acute angle)
- The line *k* has a negative slope where $90° < \theta < 180°$.   (obtuse angle)
- When $\theta = 0°$, the slope of the line is 0. This would be a horizontal line.
- When $\theta = 90°$, the slope of the line is not defined. This would be a vertical line.

Example

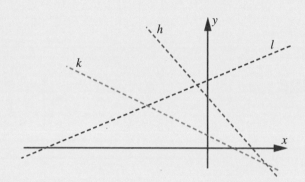

Which of the above lines have a positive slope? Justify your answer.

Solution

Mark the angles of inclination *A*, *B* and *C*, as in the diagram.

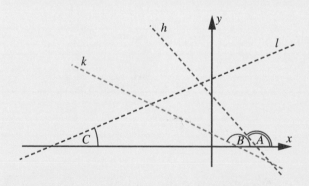

By observation, angle *C* is the only angle less than 90°.

∴ tan ∠*C* gives the only positive slope.

Since line *l* is associated with angle *C*, we conclude that line *l* has a positive slope.

exam focus

Some exam solutions may be short but wordy. Alternatively, since *l* is the only line going up (reading the graph from left to right), the slope of *l* is positive.

Example

A line crosses the x-axis at $x = 6$ and the y-axis at $y = 4$.
Find the slope of the line.

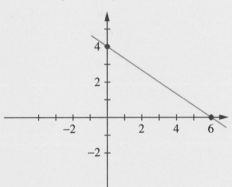

Solution

The slope of the line

$$= -\frac{\text{Rise}}{\text{Run}}$$

$$= -\frac{4}{6}$$

$$= -\frac{2}{3}$$

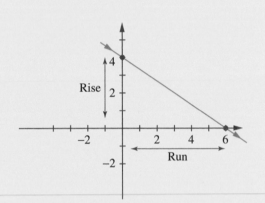

key point

In this case the slope is negative because the line goes **down** from left to right.

exam Q

The table shows temperatures in degrees Celsius and the equivalent Fahrenheit.

Celsius (°C)	50	65	80	95	100	120
Fahrenheit (°F)	122	149	176	203	212	248

(i) Show the information on a graph.

(ii) Given the relationship is linear, write it in the form $F = aC + b$, where $a, b \in \mathbb{R}$ and C, F represent the temperature in Celsius and Fahrenheit respectively.

(iii) Use the relationship to find the equivalent Fahrenheit temperature for $-30°C$.

Solution

(i)

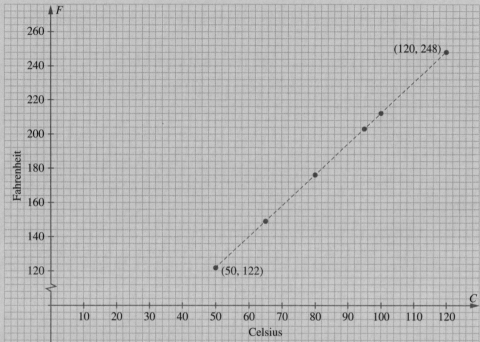

(ii) To find the equation of the line, we need its slope and one point on it.
To find the slope, we use the two extreme points: (50, 122) and (120, 248).

Slope $= m = \dfrac{y_2 - y_1}{x_2 - x_1}$ $(x_1, y_1) = (50, 122)$ and $(x_2, y_2) = (120, 248)$

$$m = \dfrac{248 - 122}{120 - 50} = \dfrac{126}{70} = \dfrac{9}{5}$$

Equation of a line: $y - y_1 = m(x - x_1)$ (see *booklet of formulae and tables*, page 18)

$$F - 122 = \frac{9}{5}(C - 50)$$

$$F - 122 = \frac{9}{5}C - 90$$

$$F = \frac{9}{5}C - 90 + 122$$

$$F = \frac{9}{5}C + 32$$

(iii) $F = \dfrac{9}{5}(-30) + 32 = -54 + 32 = -22$

This means that $-30°C = -22°F$

The slope of a line when given its equation

To find the slope of a line when given its equation, do the following.

Method 1:

> Get y on its own, and the number in front of x is the slope.

Note: The number in front of x is called the **coefficient** of x.
The number on its own is called the y **intercept**.
In short: write the line in the form $y = mx + c$.

$$y = \quad mx \quad + \quad c \qquad \text{(see \textit{booklet of formulae and tables}, page 18)}$$
$$\qquad \downarrow \qquad\qquad\qquad \downarrow$$
$$y = (\text{slope})x + (\text{where the line cuts the } y\text{-axis})$$

Method 2:

> If the line is in the form $ax + by + c = 0$, then $-\dfrac{a}{b}$ is the slope.

In words: $\qquad \text{Slope} = -\dfrac{\text{Number in front of } x}{\text{Number in front of } y}$

Note: When using this method, make sure every term is on the left-hand side in the given equation of the line.

Example

Write down the slope, m, of each of the following lines.

(i) $y = 4x - 3$ (ii) $y = 8 - 2x$ (iii) $y = x + 5$

(iv) $2y = 7x - 10$ (v) $y - 6x = 0$ (vi) $3y + 2x + 12 = 0$

Solution

Using $y = mx + c$ in each case:

(i) $y = 4x - 3 \Rightarrow m = 4$

(ii) $y = 8 - 2x \Rightarrow m = -2$ (be careful, include the minus)

(iii) $y = x + 5 \Rightarrow m = 1$ (m is not zero)

(iv) $2y = 7x - 10$ (divide each term by 2 to get)

$$y = \frac{7}{2}x - 5 \Rightarrow m = \frac{7}{2}$$

(v) $y - 6x = 0$

$$y = 6x \implies m = 6$$

(vi) $3y + 2x + 12 = 0$

$$3y = -2x - 12 \qquad \text{(divide each term by 3)}$$

$$y = \frac{-2}{3}x - 4 \implies m = -\frac{2}{3}$$

Parallel lines

To prove whether or not two lines are parallel, do the following:

1. Find the slope of each line.
2. (i) If the slopes are the same, the lines are parallel.
   (ii) If the slopes are different, the lines are **not** parallel.

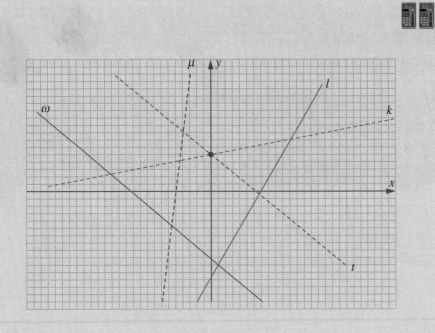

Five lines, μ, ω, t, l and k, in the coordinate plane are shown in the diagram above.

The slopes of the five lines are in the table.

Complete the table, matching the lines to their slopes.

Slope	Line
$\frac{1}{6}$	
$\frac{5}{3}$	
$-\frac{9}{10}$	
13	
$-\frac{9}{10}$	

Solution

Two lines have slope $-\frac{9}{10}$. This means two lines are parallel.

$\therefore$ t has slope $-\frac{9}{10}$ and ω has slope $-\frac{9}{10}$.

Now l, k and μ all have positive slopes (angle of inclination $< 90°$).

By observation, μ has the steepest positive slope.

$\therefore$ μ has slope 13.

Also by observation, k has the least steep positive slope.

$\therefore$ k has slope $\frac{1}{6}$.

Since the only remaining line is l and the only remaining slope is $\frac{5}{3}$ $\Rightarrow$ l has slope $\frac{5}{3}$.

Slope	Line
$\frac{1}{6}$	k
$\frac{5}{3}$	
$-\frac{9}{10}$	t
13	μ
$-\frac{9}{10}$	ω

Perpendicular lines

To prove whether or not two lines are perpendicular, do the following.

1. Find the slope of each line.
2. Multiply both slopes.
3. (i) If the answer in step 2 is -1, the lines are perpendicular.
   (ii) If the answer in step 2 is **not** -1, the lines are **not** perpendicular.

Example

The equation of two lines are:

$p: 10x + 4y - 9 = 0$ and $q: 2x - 5y + 20 = 0$.

Investigate if p is perpendicular to q.

Solution

Use $y = mx + c$ on each equation.

Slope of p:	Slope of q:
$10x + 4y - 9 = 0$	$2x - 5y + 20 = 0$
$\qquad 4y = -10x + 9$	$\qquad -5y = -2x - 20$
(divide each term by 4)	$\qquad 5y = 2x + 20$ (divide each term by 5)
$y = -\dfrac{10}{4}x + \dfrac{9}{4}$	$y = \dfrac{2}{5}x + 4$
$\therefore p$ has slope $= -\dfrac{10}{4} = -\dfrac{5}{2}$	$\therefore q$ has slope $= \dfrac{2}{5}$

$$(\text{slope of } p) \times (\text{slope of } q) = -\frac{5}{2} \times \frac{2}{5} = -1$$

Hence, line p is perpendicular to line q.

To verify that a point belongs to a line

Substitute the coordinates of the point into the equation of the line. If the coordinates satisfy the equation, then the point is on the line. Otherwise, the point is not on the line.

Example

Investigate if the points $(-2, 9)$ and $(-5, 3)$ are on the line
$5x - 3y + 34 = 0$.

Solution

$(-2, 9)$ $5x - 3y + 34 = 0$	$(-5, 3)$ $5x - 3y + 34 = 0$
Substitute $x = -2$ and $y = 9$.	Substitute $x = -5$ and $y = 3$.
$\quad 5(-2) - 3(9) + 34$	$\quad 5(-5) - 3(3) + 34$
$\quad = -10 - 27 + 34$	$\quad = -25 - 9 + 34$
$\quad = -37 + 34$	$\quad = -34 + 34$
$\quad = -3 \neq 0$	$\quad = 0$
Does not satisfy the equation.	Satisfies the equation.
$\therefore (-2, 9)$ is not on the line.	$\therefore (-5, 3)$ is on the line.

Example

(i) The point $(k, -2)$ is on the line $4x + 3y - 14 = 0$. Find the value of k.

(ii) The point $(1, 2)$ is on the line $3x + ty - 11 = 0$. Find the value of t.

Solution

(i) $4x + 3y - 14 = 0$

Substitute $x = k$ and $y = -2$.

$(k, -2)$: $4(k) + 3(-2) - 14 = 0$

$4k - 6 - 14 = 0$

$4k - 20 = 0$

$4k = 20$

$k = 5$

(ii) $3x + ty - 11 = 0$

Substitute $x = 1$ and $y = 2$.

$(1, 2)$: $3(1) + t(2) - 11 = 0$

$3 + 2t - 11 = 0$

$2t - 8 = 0$

$2t = 8$

$t = 4$

Graphing lines

To draw a line, only two points are needed. The easiest points to find are where lines cut the x- and y-axes. This is known as the **intercept method**.

On the x-axis, y = 0. On the y-axis, x = 0.

To draw a line, do the following:

1. Let $y = 0$ and find x.
2. Let $x = 0$ and find y.
3. Plot these two points.
4. Draw the line through these points.

If the constant in the equation of a line is zero, e.g. $3x - 5y = 0$, or $4x = 3y$, then the line will pass through the origin, $(0, 0)$. In this case, the **intercept method** will not work.

To draw a line that contains the origin, $(0, 0)$, do the following:

1. Choose a suitable value for x and find the corresponding value for y (or vice versa).
2. Plot this point.
3. A line drawn through this point and the origin is the required line.

key point

A suitable method is to let x equal the number in front of y and then find the corresponding value for y (or vice versa).

exam Q

(2016 Q.4)

(a) The line l contains the points $A(4, 5)$ and $B(2, 0)$. Find the equation of l. Give your answer in the form $ax + by + c = 0$ where a, b, and $c \in \mathbb{Z}$.
(b) Draw the line k: $x + 2y = 8$ on a coordinated plane.

Solution

(a) Slope $AB = m = \dfrac{y_2 - y_1}{x_2 - x_1}$ $A = (4, 5) = (x_1y_1)$ $B = (2, 0) = (x_2y_2)$

Slope $AB = m = \dfrac{0 - 5}{2 - 4} = \dfrac{-5}{-2} = \dfrac{5}{2}$

Equation of AB given by $y - y_1 = m(x - x_1)$

Sub in for x_1, y_1 and m to get:

$$y - 5 = \frac{5}{2}(x - 4)$$
$$2(y - 5) = 5(x - 4) \qquad \text{(multiply both sides by 2)}$$
$$2y - 10 = 5x - 20$$
$$0 = 5x - 2y - 10$$
$5x - 2y - 10 = 0$ as required.

(b) To draw k: $x + 2y = 8$, find the points where the line cuts the x and y axes

Let $x = 0$	Let $y = 0$
Then $0 + 2y = 8$	Then $x + 0 = 8$
$2y = 8$	$x = 8$
$y = 4$	
$(0, 4)$	$(8, 0)$

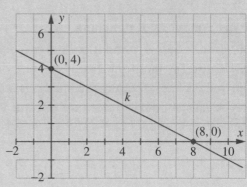

Lines parallel to the axes

$x = 2$ is a line parallel to the y-axis through 2 on the x-axis.

$y = -1$ is a line parallel to the x-axis through -1 on the y-axis.

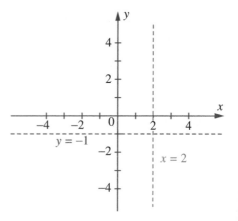

$y = 0$ is the equation of the x-axis.
$x = 0$ is the equation of the y-axis.

All horizontal lines (parallel to the x-axis) have an angle of inclination of 0° and their slopes are zero.

All vertical lines (parallel to the y-axis) have an angle of inclination of 90° and their slopes are infinitely steep.

The exam may contain a question incorporating transformations of the plane and coordinate geometry. To answer such a question, candidates should be aware of the following.

Transformations of the plane:

 (i) **Translation:** A translation moves a point in a straight line.
 (ii) **Central symmetry:** Central symmetry is a reflection in a point.
(iii) **Axial symmetry:** Axial symmetry is a reflection in a line.
(iv) **Axial symmetry in the axes or central symmetry in the origin.**

The following three patterns emerge and it is worth memorising them:

1. Axial symmetry in the x-axis → **change the sign of y.**
2. Axial symmetry in the y-axis → **change the sign of x.**
3. Central symmetry in the origin, (0, 0) → **change the sign of both x and y.**

Alternatively, plot the point on the coordinated plane and use your knowledge of axial symmetry and central symmetry to find the image.

Given the point $(3, -4)$ is on the line $l: 7x - 2y - 29 = 0$, find the equation of the image of l under the translation $(0, 2) \rightarrow (-1, 5)$.

Solution

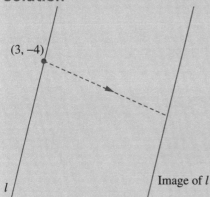

$(3, -4)$

Image of l

l

$(0, 2) \rightarrow (-1, 5)$

Rule: Take 1 from x, add 3 to y.

$\therefore \quad (3, -4) \rightarrow (3 - 1, -4 + 3) = (2, -1)$

key point

A translation maps a line onto a parallel line.

Since parallel lines have equal slopes, the image of l has the form

$\qquad 7x - 2y + k = 0 \qquad$ where $k \in \mathbb{R}$.

We know $(2, -1) \in 7x - 2y + k = 0$

$\qquad \therefore 7(2) - 2(-1) + k = 0$

$\qquad\qquad 14 + 2 + k = 0$

$\qquad\qquad\quad 16 + k = 0$

$\qquad\qquad\qquad k = -16$

Equation of image of $l: 7x - 2y - 16 = 0$.

exam focus

Alternatively find the slope of the given line and use that slope with $(2, -1)$ to find the equation of the parallel line.

$A(4, 1)$ and $B(7, k)$ are two points. If $|AB| = 5$, find the two values of k.

Solution

$A(4, 1) \qquad B(7, k)$

$(x_1, y_1) \qquad (x_2, y_2)$

Given: $\hspace{4cm} |AB| = 5$

$\therefore \sqrt{(x_2 - x_1)^2 + (y_2 - y_1)^2} = 5$

$\therefore \quad (x_2 - x_1)^2 + (y_2 - y_1)^2 = 25$ (squaring both sides removes $\sqrt{\,}$)

$\therefore \quad (7 - 4)^2 + (k - 1)^2 = 25$ (put in $x_2 = 7$, $x_1 = 4$, $y_2 = k$ and $y_1 = 1$)

$\quad (3)^2 + (k^2 - 2k + 1) = 25$ $\quad ((k - 1)^2 = k^2 - 2k + 1)$

$\quad 9 + k^2 - 2k + 1 = 25$

$\quad k^2 - 2k + 10 = 25$ (simplify the left-hand side)

$\quad k^2 - 2k - 15 = 0$ (subtract 25 from both sides)

$\quad (k + 3)(k - 5) = 0$ (factorise)

$k + 3 = 0 \quad$ or $\quad k - 5 = 0$

$k = -3 \quad$ or $\quad k = 5$

Notice that factorising from algebra may be required to complete a coordinate geometry question.

(2017 Q.8)

The diagram below shows the triangles *CBA* and *CDE*.

(a) The coordinates of *C* are (4·5, 0).

From the diagram, write down the coordinates of the points *A*, *B*, *D* and *E*.

$A = ($, $)$
$B = ($, $)$
$D = ($, $)$
$E = ($, $)$

(b) Show, using slopes, that the line segments [*AB*] and [*DE*] are parallel.

(c) **(i)** Show that the area of the triangle *CBA* is 4 square units.

(ii) Find |*AB*|, the distance from *A* to *B*.

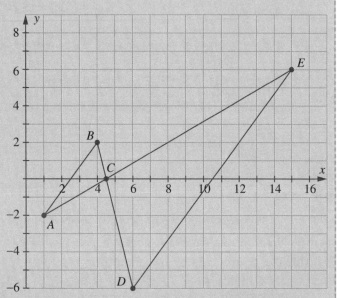

Solution

(a) $A = (1, -2)$

$B = (4, 2)$

$D = (6, -6)$

$E = (15, 6)$

(b) Slope $AB = \dfrac{y_2 - y_1}{x_2 - x_1}$

$(x_1 y_1) = (1, -2)$
$(x_2 y_2) = (4, 2)$

$$= \frac{2 - (-2)}{4 - 1} = \frac{4}{3}$$

Slope $DE = \dfrac{y_2 - y_1}{x_2 - x_1}$

$(x_1 y_1) = (6, -6)$
$(x_2 y_2) = (15, 6)$

$$= \frac{6 - (-6)}{15 - 6} = \frac{12}{9} = \frac{4}{3}$$

key point

Parallel lines have equal slopes.

Since slope $AB = \dfrac{4}{3} =$ slope DE, we know that *AB* is parallel to *DE*.

(c) (i) Area $\triangle CBA$ given by $\frac{1}{2}|x_1y_2 - x_2y_1|$

$A = (1, -2) \rightarrow (0, 0)$

$B = (4, 2) \rightarrow (3, 4) = (x_1y_1)$

Use a translation to map any one point to (0, 0). Apply the same translation to the other points.

$C = \left(4 \cdot 5, 0\right) \rightarrow \left(3 \cdot 5, 2\right) = (x_2y_2)$

Area $\triangle ABC = \frac{1}{2}|(3)(2) - (3\cdot5)(4)| = \frac{1}{2}|6 - 14| = \frac{1}{2}|-8| = 4$ square units

(ii) $|AB| = \sqrt{(x_2 - x_1)^2 + (y_2 - y_1)^2}$ where $(x_1y_1) = (1, -2)$

and $(x_2y_2) = (4, 2)$

$|AB| = \sqrt{(4 - 1)^2 + (2 - (-2))^2} = \sqrt{3^2 + 4^2} = \sqrt{9 + 16} = 5$ units

---

exam Q

(2015 Q.2)

The line p makes equal intercepts on the axes at A and B, as shown.

(a) (i) Write down the slope of p.

(ii) The point (1, 5) is on p. Find the equation of p.

Write your answer in the form $ax + by + c = 0$, where a, b and $c \in \mathbb{Z}$.

(b) The line q is perpendicular to p and contains the point O (0, 0). Find the equation of q.

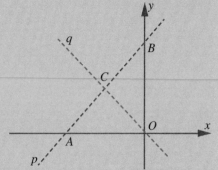

Solution

(a) (i)

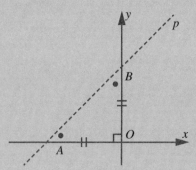

Equal intercepts means $|OA| = |OB|$

Hence from diagram • = 45° (isosceles triangle)

Slope $p = \tan 45° = 1$

(ii) Use $y - y_1 = m(x - x_1)$ where $m = 1 = $ slope p $(x_1 y_1) = (1, 5)$

$\qquad y - 5 = 1(x - 1)$

$\qquad y - 5 = x - 1$

$\quad x - y + 4 = 0$

(b) q perpendicular to p means

$\quad$ (slope of p)(slope of q) $= -1$

$\qquad$ (1)(slope of q) $= -1$

$\qquad\qquad$ slope of $q = -1$

Use $y - y_1 = m(x - x_1)$ with $m = -1$ and $(x_1 y_1) = (0, 0)$

$\quad y - 0 = -1(x - 0)$

$\qquad y = -x$ is the equation of q.

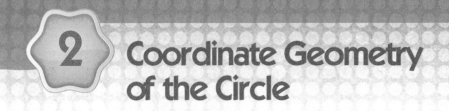

2 Coordinate Geometry of the Circle

Definitions

A circle is a set of points (a locus), each of which is equidistant from a fixed point called the **centre**.

The distance from the centre to any point on the circle is called the **radius**.

The centre, C, of a wind turbine and the tip of a blade, P, are indicated on the diagram.

The path (locus) traced out in one revolution of P is a circle, centre C, with radius $|CP|$.

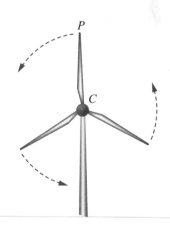

The equation of a circle

Circle with centre (0, 0)

Two quantities are needed to find the equation of a circle.

> **1.** Centre   **2.** Radius
>
> If the centre is (0, 0), the equation of the circle will be of the form $x^2 + y^2 = r^2$.

Circle with centre (h, k)

Two quantities are needed to find the equation of a circle.

> **1.** Centre, (h, k) **2.** Radius, r
>
> Then use the formula $(x - h)^2 + (y - k)^2 = r^2$.
>
> (see *booklet of formulae and tables* page 19)

key point

When we talk about the 'equation of a circle', we should really say 'the equation of the circumference of the circle'.

Example

Find the centre and radius of the following circles.

(i) $x^2 + y^2 = 9$

(ii) $(x - 3)^2 + (y + 4)^2 = 40$

Solution

(i) $x^2 + y^2 = 9$

Centre $= (0, 0)$

Radius $= \sqrt{9} = 3$

(ii) $(x - 3)^2 + (y + 4)^2 = 40$

Centre $= (3, -4)$

Radius $= \sqrt{40} = \sqrt{(4)(10)} = 2\sqrt{10}$

Example

A circle with centre $(0, 0)$ passes through the point $(-3, 1)$.
Find the equation of the circle.

Solution

We have the centre and require the radius.

Radius, $r =$ distance between the points $(0, 0)$ and $(-3, 1)$.

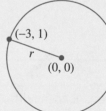

$$r = \sqrt{(x_2 - x_1)^2 + (y_2 - y_1)^2}$$

$$r = \sqrt{(-3 - 0)^2 + (1 - 0)^2} = \sqrt{9 + 1} = \sqrt{10}$$

Equation of the circle: $(x - h)^2 + (y - k)^2 = r^2$

$$(x - 0)^2 + (y - 0)^2 = \left(\sqrt{10}\right)^2$$

$$x^2 + y^2 = 10$$

Points inside, on or outside a circle

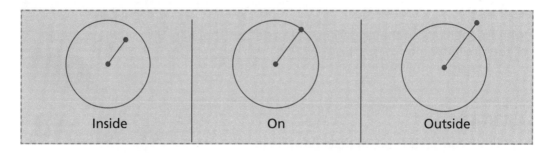

Inside | On | Outside

In coordinate geometry of the line, to determine if a point is on a line you substitute the coordinates of the point into the equation of the line. The same method is used in this chapter.

We substitute the coordinates of the given point in for x and y into the equation of the circle.

$$(x - h)^2 + (y - k)^2 = r^2$$

If   LHS $<$ RHS: The point is **inside** the circle.

LHS $=$ RHS: The point is **on** the circle.

LHS $>$ RHS: The point is **outside** the circle.

key point

LHS means 'left hand side', RHS means 'right hand side'.

exam focus

Remember the difference between a **circle** and a **disc**. A circle is similar to a ring, while a disc is similar to a dinner plate. Therefore, a disc contains all the points on the edge **and** those within that boundary. A circle would refer only to those edge points.

The phrase 'The circle contains the point P ...' means that P is **on** the circumference of the circle rather than being a point enclosed by it.

Example

(i) $x^2 + y^2 = 11$ is the equation of a circle k. Determine whether $(-2, 3)$ is inside, on or outside k.

(ii) $(x - 7)^2 + y^2 = 3$ is the equation of a circle c. Determine whether $(8, -1)$ is inside, on or outside c.

Solution

(i) $x^2 + y^2 = 11$

$(-2, 3)$: $\quad (-2)^2 + (3)^2$

$= 4 + 9$

$= 13 > 11$

$\therefore (-2, 3)$ is outside k.

(ii) $(x - 7)^2 + y^2 = 3$

$(8, -1)$: $\quad (8 - 7)^2 + (-1)^2$

$= 1 + 1$

$= 2 < 3$

$\therefore (8, -1)$ is inside c.

Example

The circle $(x + 1)^2 + (y - k)^2 = 10$ contains the origin $(0, 0)$.
Find the possible values of k.

Solution

Since the point $(0, 0)$ is on the circle, substitute $x = 0$ and $y = 0$ into

$$(x + 1)^2 + (y - k)^2 = 10$$

To get $\quad (0 + 1)^2 + (0 - k)^2 = 10$

$$1 + k^2 = 10$$

$$k^2 = 9$$

We have two choices of methods to solve for k.

Method 1

$$k^2 = 9$$
$$k^2 - 9 = 0$$
$$(k - 3)(k + 3) = 0$$
$\therefore k - 3 = 0$ $\boxed{\text{or}}$ $k + 3 = 0$

$\quad k = 3$ $\boxed{\text{or}}$ $\quad k = -3$

Method 2

$$k^2 = 9$$
$$k = \pm\sqrt{9}$$
$$k = \pm 3$$

Equation of a tangent to a circle at a given point

A tangent is perpendicular to the radius that joins the centre
of a circle to the point of tangency.

This fact is used to find the slope of the tangent.

In the diagram on the right, the radius, r, is perpendicular
to the tangent, t, at the point of tangency, P.

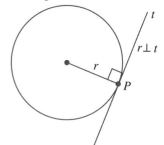

The equation of a tangent to a circle at a given point is found with the following steps:

1. Find the slope of the radius to the point of tangency.
2. Turn this slope upside down and change its sign. This gives the slope of the tangent.
3. To find the equation of the tangent, use the coordinates of the point of contact and the slope of the tangent in the formula:

$$y - y_1 = m(x - x_1)$$

Note: A diagram is often very useful.

Example

Find the equation of the tangent to the circle $x^2 + y^2 = 10$ at the
point $(-3, -1)$.

Solution

The centre of the circle $x^2 + y^2 = 10$ is $(0, 0)$.

Slope of indicated diameter, d, containing $(0, 0)$
and $(-3, -1)$

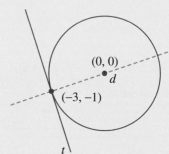

$$= \frac{y_2 - y_1}{x_2 - x_1} = \frac{0 - (-1)}{0 - (-3)} = \frac{1}{3}$$

Since diameter, d, is perpendicular to the tangent, t, at the point of contact $(-3, -1)$,
the slope of the tangent $= -\frac{3}{1} = -3 = m$.

For perpendicular lines, the product of their slopes is -1 or $(m_1)(m_2) = -1$.
In this example, $\left(\frac{1}{3}\right)(-3) = -1$.

Equation of tangent given by $y - y_1 = m(x - x_1)$ where $m = -3$.

$$(x_1, y_1) = (-3, -1) \qquad\qquad y - (-1) = -3(x - (-3))$$
$$y + 1 = -3(x + 3)$$
$$y + 1 = -3x - 9$$
$$y + 3x + 10 = 0$$

A circle has centre (2, 4) and touches the y-axis. Find the equation of the circle.

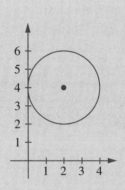

The word 'touch' in coordinate geometry often means a tangent is involved.

Solution

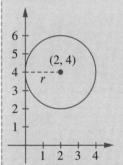

Radius $= r = |2| = 2$ (by observation from the diagram)

Equation of circle is

$$(x - 2)^2 + (y - 4)^2 = (2)^2$$
$$(x - 2)^2 + (y - 4)^2 = 4$$

A diagram can often have the information needed for success with the solution. Always examine the diagram given and attempt to identify any useful or relevant information.

The diagram shows four circles of equal radii. The circles are touching, as shown.

The equation of c_1 is $x^2 + y^2 = 9$.

- **(i)** Write down the radius of c_1.
- **(ii)** Write down the coordinates of the centre of c_3.
- **(iii)** Write down the equation of c_3.

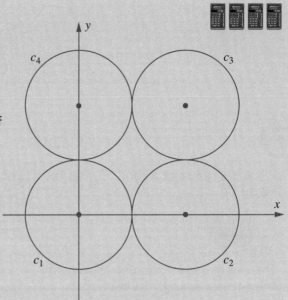

Solution

(i) Radius of $c_1 = \sqrt{9} = 3$.

(ii) From the diagram given, the radius of each circle is 3 so the centre of $c_3 = (6, 6)$.

(iii) Equation of c_3 is

$$(x - 6)^2 + (y - 6)^2 = (3)^2$$
$$(x - 6)^2 + (y - 6)^2 = 9$$

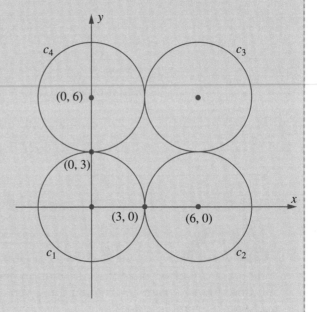

Length of a tangent to a circle from a point outside the circle

The **length of a tangent** from a point outside a circle is the distance, d, from the point outside the circle to the point of tangency.

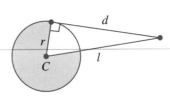

1. Find the centre, C, and radius length, r, of the circle.
2. Find the distance, l, between the centre and the point outside the circle.
3. Use Pythagoras' theorem to find d, i.e. $l^2 = r^2 + d^2$.

$x^2 + y^2 = 121$ is the equation of a circle, k.

(a) Write down the centre, C, and the radius of k.

(b) PQ is a tangent to the circle k.

C is the centre of k.

P has coordinates $(-12, 5)$.

(i) On the diagram, join [CQ] and join [PC].

(ii) Find $|PC|$.

(iii) Hence, find $|PQ|$ in the form $a\sqrt{h}$ where $a, h \in \mathbb{N}$.

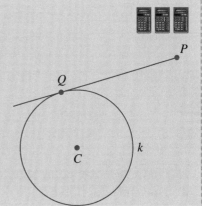

Solution

(a) $C = (0,0)$ and radius $\sqrt{121} = 11$.

(b) (i)

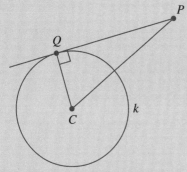

(ii) $|PC| = \sqrt{(x_2 - x_1)^2 - (y_2 - y_1)^2}$

where $(x_1 y_1) = (0,0)$ and $(x_2 y_2) = (-12,5)$

$|PC| = \sqrt{(-12 - 0)^2 - (5 - 0)^2}$

$\quad = \sqrt{144 + 25} = \sqrt{169} = 13$

(iii) $|PC|^2 = |QC|^2 + |PQ|^2$

$\quad (13)^2 = (11)^2 + |PQ|^2$

$\quad 169 = 121 + |PQ|^2$

$\quad 48 = |PQ|^2$

$\quad 4\sqrt{3} = |PQ|$

key point

Tangent is perpendicular to radius at point of contact.

Circles intersecting the axes

To find where a circle intersects the axes, we use the following.

> The circle intersects the x-axis at $y = 0$.
> The circle intersects the y-axis at $x = 0$.

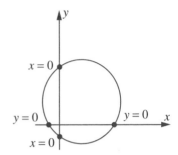

$A(3, 5)$ and $B(-1, -1)$ are the end points of a diameter of a circle s.

(i) Find the centre and radius length of s.

(ii) Find the equation of s.

(iii) s intersects the x-axis at P and Q, $P < Q$. Find the coordinates of P and Q.

Solution

(i) Centre is the midpoint of $[AB]$.

   $A(3, 5)$ $B(-1, -1)$

The midpoint of $[AB] = \left(\dfrac{3-1}{2}, \dfrac{5-1}{2}\right) = (1, 2)$.

The radius is the distance from $(1, 2)$ to $(3, 5)$ or $(-1, -1)$.

Thus, the radius $= \sqrt{(3-1)^2 + (5-2)^2} = \sqrt{2^2 + 3^2} = \sqrt{13}$.

Centre $= (1, 2)$ and radius $= \sqrt{13}$.

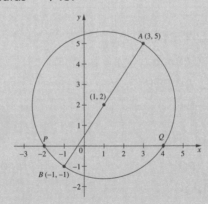

(ii) Centre $= (1, 2)$ and radius $= \sqrt{13}$.

$(x - h)^2 + (y - k)^2 = r^2$

$(x - 1)^2 + (y - 2)^2 = \left(\sqrt{13}\right)^2$

$(x - 1)^2 + (y - 2)^2 = 13$

(iii) On the *x*-axis, *y* = 0.

$$(x - 1)^2 + (y - 2)^2 = 13$$
$$(x - 1)^2 + (0 - 2)^2 = 13 \qquad \text{(substitute } y = 0\text{)}$$
$$(x - 1)^2 + 4 = 13$$
$$(x - 1)^2 = 9 \qquad \text{(take the square root of both sides)}$$
$$x - 1 = \pm 3$$

$x - 1 = +3$ or $x - 1 = -3$

$x = 4$ or $x = -2$

∴ $P = (-2, 0)$ and $Q = (4, 0)$ are the required points since $P < Q$.

key point

The points $P(-2, 0)$ and $Q(4, 0)$ are called the intercepts of the circle *s* and the *x*-axis. In mathematics, an intercept is a point at which two figures intersect.

Intersection of a line and a circle

If a line and a circle are drawn on the plane, then the line and circle may meet at two points or at one point, or they may not meet at all. The diagrams below illustrate these three different situations.

Two points of intersection

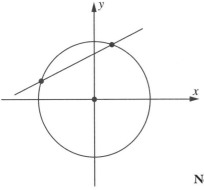

One point of intersection

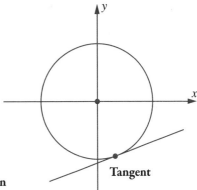

No points of intersection

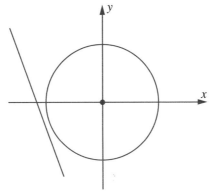

key point

If the line meets the circle at one point only, then we say the line is a tangent to the circle.

To find the points where a line and a circle meet, the method of substitution between their equations is used.

The method involves the following three steps:

1. Get x or y on its own from the equation of the line.
   (Look carefully and select the variable which will make the work easier.)
2. Substitute for this same variable into the equation of the circle and solve the resultant quadratic equation.
3. Substitute separately the value(s) obtained in step 2 into the linear equation in step 1 to find the corresponding value(s) of the other variable.

exam Q

A plane is travelling along the line $x + y - 5 = 0$. Ahead lies a large cloud of ash from a volcanic eruption that can be represented by the circle $x^2 + y^2 = 17$.

Note: Each unit represents 1 kilometre.

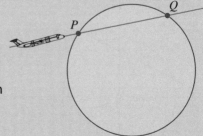

(i) Find the coordinates of the points P and Q.

(ii) If it is considered unsafe to travel more than 4 km through such an ash cloud, should the plane alter its course? Justify your answer.

Solution

(i) $x + y - 5 = 0$ and $x^2 + y^2 = 17$

$x = 5 - y$
$x^2 = (5 - y)^2$
$x^2 = 25 - 10y + y^2$

$(25 - 10y + y^2) + y^2 = 17$
$2y^2 - 10y + 8 = 0$
$y^2 - 5y + 4 = 0$
$(y - 4)(y - 1) = 0$

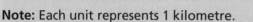

$y - 4 = 0$ or $y - 1 = 0$

$y = 4$ or $y = 1$

If $y = 4$ then $x = 5 - y$

$x = 5 - 4$

$x = 1$

One point of intersection is $(1, 4)$.

If $y = 1$ then $x = 5 - y$

$x = 5 - 1$

$x = 4$

Another point of intersection is $(4, 1)$.

The sentence 'The above work is my justification' will be very useful and worthwhile in the examination itself. You can use the sentence whenever you are asked to justify your answer and you have shown relevant work.

(ii) $|PQ| = \sqrt{(x_2 - x_1)^2 + (y_2 - y_1)^2}$

$(1, 4) = (x_1, y_1)$

$(4, 1) = (x_2, y_2)$

$|PQ| = \sqrt{(4 - 1)^2 + (1 - 4)^2} = \sqrt{9 + 9} = \sqrt{18} = 4{\cdot}242640687$

$\therefore$ $|PQ| = 4{\cdot}24$ km > 4 km

Yes, the plane should alter its course.

The work above is my justification.

(2016 Q.3)

(a) The circle c has centre $(2, -3)$ and a radius of 4 cm.

Write down the equation of c.

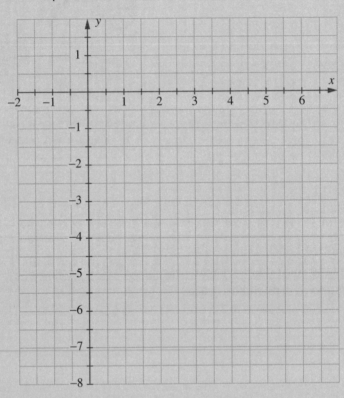

(b) Draw the circle c on the grid. Each unit on the coordinate grid is 1 cm.

(c) Verify, using algebra, that the point $(3, 1)$ is outside of c.

(d) Find the area of the smallest four-sided figure that will fit around the circle c.

Solution

(a) $(x - h)^2 + (y - k)^2 = r^2$, where $(2, -3) = (h, k)$ and $4 = r$

$(x - 2)^2 + (y + 3)^2 = 4^2$

$(x - 2)^2 + (y + 3)^2 = 16$ is the equation of the circle c.

(b)

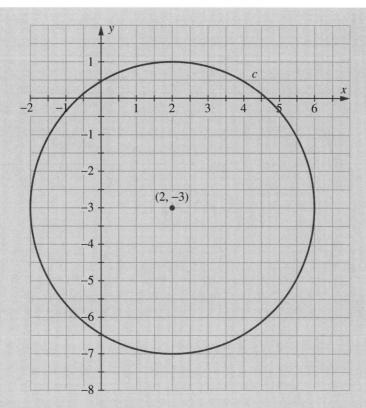

(c) Is $(3, 1) \in (x - 2)^2 + (y + 3)^2 = 16$

$(3 - 2)^2 + (1 + 3)^2 = 16$

$1 + 16 > 16$, so $(3, 1)$ is outside the circle.

(d)

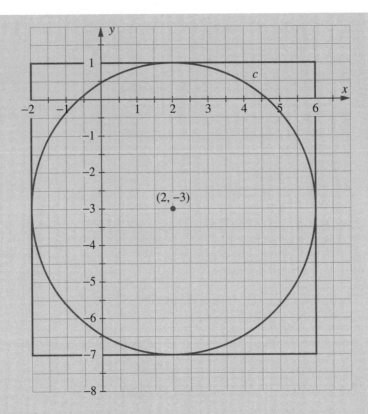

Radius of circle $c = 4$, which means the diameter = 8 cm.

Smallest box is a square of sides 8 cm.

Area = $8 \times 8 = 64$ cm^2

This question was awarded a total of 25 marks, however the marking scheme was not kind to errors.

Part **(a)** was worth 5 marks, minus 3 marks for any error.

Part **(b)** was worth 5 marks, minus 3 marks for any error.

Part **(c)** was worth 10 marks, minus 6 marks for any error.

Part **(d)** was worth 5 marks, minus 3 marks for any error.

It is vital to keep your concentration.

(2017 Q.2)

(a) The circle c has centre $(0, 0)$ and radius 5 units. Write down the equation of c.

(b) The diagram shows a semi-circle which is part of c.

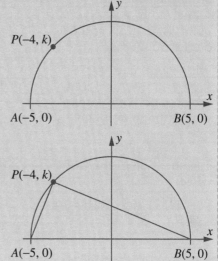

(i) The point $P(-4, k)$, $k > 0$ is on the semi-circle. Find the value of k.

(ii) Show that the triangle ABP is right-angled at P.

(c) Find the area of the region which is inside the semi-circle but outside the triangle ABP. Give your answer, in square units, correct to two decimal places.

Solution

(a) $x^2 + y^2 = 25$

(b) (i) Substitute $(-4, k)$ into
$$x^2 + y^2 = 25$$
$$(-4)^2 + k^2 = 25$$
$$k^2 = 9$$
$$k = \pm 3$$

However, given $k > 0$ in question, answer is $k = 3$.

(ii) Slope PA Slope PB

$(-4, 3)$ and $(-5, 0)$ $(5, 0)$ and $(-4, 3)$

Slope $PA = m_1 = \dfrac{0 - 3}{-5 - (-4)}$ Slope $PB = m_2 = \dfrac{3 - 0}{-4 - 5} = \dfrac{3}{-9}$

$= \dfrac{-3}{-1} = 3$ $= -\dfrac{1}{3}$

$(m_1)(m_2) = (3)\left(-\dfrac{1}{3}\right) = -1$ indicates $PA \perp PB$

(c) Area semi-circle $= \dfrac{1}{2}\pi r^2 = \dfrac{1}{2}\pi(5)^2 = 12 \cdot 5\pi$

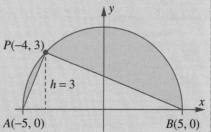

Area $\triangle APB$
$= \dfrac{1}{2}(\text{base})(\perp \text{height}) = \dfrac{1}{2}(10)(3) = 15$

Shaded area $=$ area semi-circle $-$ area $\triangle APB$

$= 12 \cdot 5\pi - 15 = 24 \cdot 27$ square units

exam
Q

A penny-farthing bicycle on display in a museum is supported by a stand at points A and C. A and C lie on the front wheel.

With coordinate axes as shown and 1 unit = 5 cm, the equation of the rear wheel (the small wheel) is

$x^2 + (y - 3)^2 = 9$.

The equation of the front wheel is

$(x - 14)^2 + (y - 10)^2 = 100$.

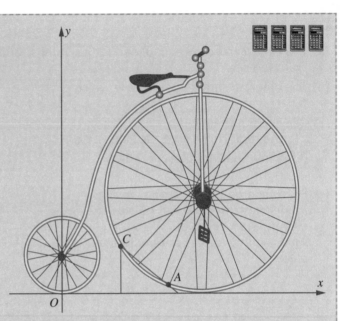

(i) Write down the coordinates of the centre and radius of the small wheel.

(ii) Write down the coordinates of the centre and radius of the big wheel.

(iii) Find the distance between the centres of the two wheels, correct to the nearest mm.

(iv) Show that the overall length of the bicycle is 1·35 m. All calculations must be clearly shown.

Solution

(i) $x^2 + (y - 3)^2 = 9$ has centre $(0, 3)$ and radius $= \sqrt{9} = 3$.

(ii) $(x - 14)^2 + (y - 10)^2 = 100$ has centre $(14, 10)$ and radius $= \sqrt{100} = 10$.

(iii) Distance from $(0, 3)$ to $(14, 10)$ is given by

$$\sqrt{(x_2 - x_1)^2 + (y_2 - y_1)^2} = \sqrt{(14 - 0)^2 + (10 - 3)^2} = \sqrt{196 + 49}$$

$$= \sqrt{245} = 15{\cdot}65247$$

1 unit = 5 cm $\Rightarrow$ Distance = 15·65247 × 5 = 78·26235 cm

= 782·6235 mm

= 783 mm (to nearest mm)

(iv)

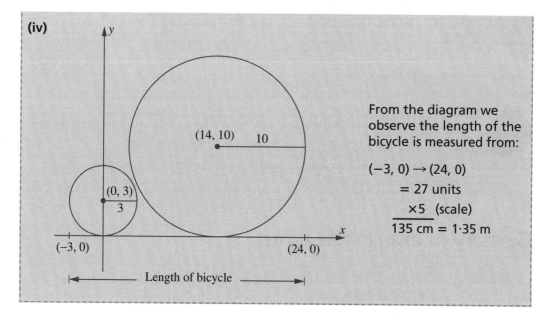

From the diagram we observe the length of the bicycle is measured from:

$(-3, 0) \rightarrow (24, 0)$

= 27 units

×5 (scale)

135 cm = 1·35 m

3 Geometry Theorems

aims

- ☐ To understand and learn the meaning of the words listed in the glossary
- ☐ To be familiar with the axioms, corollaries and theorems
- ☐ To be able to solve problems applying the axioms, corollaries and theorems

Glossary of examinable terms

Axiom:	An axiom is a statement which is assumed to be true. It can be accepted without a proof and used as a basis for an argument.
Converse:	The converse of a theorem is formed by taking the conclusion as the starting point and having the starting point as the conclusion.
Corollary:	A corollary follows after a theorem and is a statement that must be true because of that theorem.
Implies:	Implies indicates a logical relationship between two statements, such that if the first is true then the second must be true.
Is congruent to:	Two things are said to be congruent if they are identical in size and shape.
Proof:	A proof is a sequence of statements (made up of axioms, assumptions and arguments) that follow logically from the preceding one, starting at an axiom or previously proven theorem and ending with the statement of the theorem to be proven.
Theorem:	A theorem is a statement which has been proved to be true, deduced from axioms by logical argument.

exam focus

You must learn these definitions and be able to reproduce them in the exam.

You are required to know the following axioms, theorems and corollaries and you must be able to apply them in answering geometric questions.

Axioms

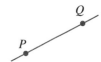

Axiom 1: There is exactly one line through any two given points.

Axiom 2: **Ruler axiom**

The distance between points P and Q has the following properties:

1. The distance $|PQ|$ is never negative.
2. The distance between two points is the same whether we measure from P to Q or from Q to P.
3. If there exists some point R between P and Q, then the distance from P to Q is equal to the sum of the distances from P to R and R to Q.

$$|PR| + |RQ| = |PQ|$$

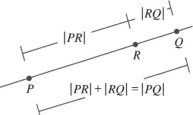

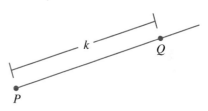

4. Marking off a distance
   Given any ray from P, and given any real number $k \geq 0$, there is a unique point Q on the ray whose distance from P is k.

Axiom 3: **Protractor axiom**

The number of degrees in an angle (also known as its degree-measure) is always a number between 0° and 360°.
It has these properties:

1. A straight angle has 180°.
2. If we know the angle $A°$, opened up at a point P, then there are two possible rays from P that form that angle.

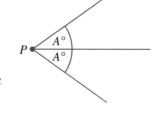

3. If an angle is divided into two, then that angle is equal to the sum of the two angles that make it up.

$$|\angle QPR| = |\angle QPS| + |\angle SPR|$$
$$|\angle QPR| = A° + B°$$

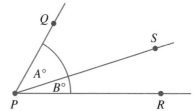

Axiom 4: **Congruent triangles**

We can say that two triangles are congruent if:

1. SAS: Two sides and the angle in between are the same in both.
2. ASA: Two angles and a side are the same in both.

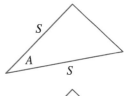

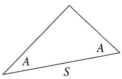

3. SSS: All three sides are the same in both.

4. RHS: Right angle, hypotenuse and another side.

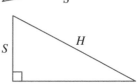

Axiom 5: Given any line *l* and a point *P*, there is exactly one line through *P* that is parallel to *l*.

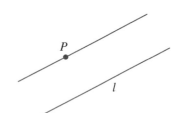

You may be asked to state an axiom in your exam, so make sure that you know at least one of them off by heart.

Theorems

- The application of all theorems can be examined.
- You will be presented with the worded statement of the theorem, without reference to the theorem number.
- Proofs are expected to begin with a diagram, followed by the following headings: 'Given', 'To prove', 'Construction' and 'Proof'.
- You must explain all construction steps fully.

Theorem 1: **Vertically opposite angles**
Vertically opposite angles are equal in measure.

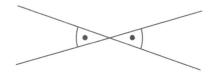

Theorem 2: **Isosceles triangles**
1. In an isosceles triangle, the angles opposite the equal sides are equal.
2. Conversely, if two angles are equal, then the triangle is isosceles.

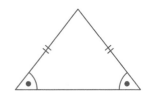

Theorem 3: **Alternate angles**
If a transversal makes equal alternate angles on two lines, then the lines are parallel (and converse).

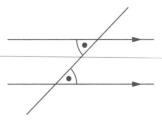

Theorem 4: **Angles in a triangle**

The angles in any triangle add up to 180°.

$$A° + B° + C° = 180°$$

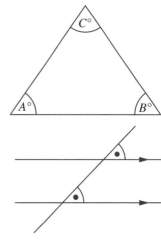

Theorem 5: **Corresponding angles**

Two lines are parallel if, and only if, for any transversal, the corresponding angles are equal.

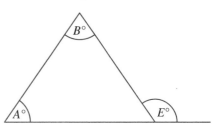

Theorem 6: **Exterior angle**

Each exterior angle of a triangle is equal to the sum of the interior opposite angles.

$$E° = A° + B°$$

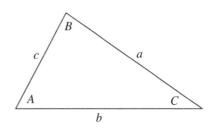

Theorem 7: **Angle–side relationship**

1. In a triangle, the angle opposite the greater of two sides is greater than the angle opposite the lesser side.
2. Conversely, the side opposite the greater of two angles is greater than the side opposite the lesser angle.

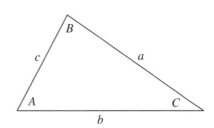

Theorem 8: **Triangle inequality**

Two sides of a triangle are together greater than the third.

$$a + b > c$$
$$b + c > a$$
$$a + c > b$$

Theorem 9: **Parallelograms**

In a parallelogram, opposite sides are equal and opposite angles are equal. Two converses of this theorem are true:

1. If the opposite angles of a quadrilateral are equal, then it is a parallelogram.
2. If the opposite sides of a quadrilateral are equal, then it is a parallelogram.

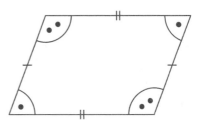

Corollary: A diagonal divides a parallelogram into two congruent triangles.

Theorem 10: Diagonals of a parallelogram
The diagonals of a parallelogram bisect each other.

Converse:
If the diagonals of a quadrilateral bisect one another, then it is a parallelogram.

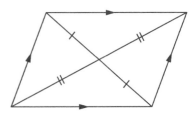

Theorem 11: Transversals
If three parallel lines cut off equal segments on some transversal line, then they will cut off equal segments on any other transversal.

Theorem 12: Proportional sides
Let *ABC* be a triangle. If a line *XY* is parallel to *BC* and cuts [*AB*] in the ratio *s* : *t*, then it also cuts [*AC*] in the same ratio.

Converse:
If a line *XY* cuts the sides *AB* and *AC* in the same ratio, then it is parallel to *BC*.

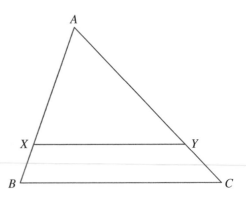

Theorem 13: Similar triangles
If two triangles are similar, then their sides are proportional, in order.

$$\frac{|PQ|}{|AB|} = \frac{|PR|}{|AC|} = \frac{|QR|}{|BC|}$$

Converse:
If the corresponding sides of two triangles are proportional, then they are similar.

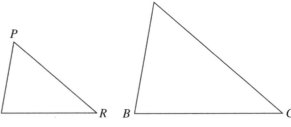

Theorem 14: Theorem of Pythagoras
In a right-angled triangle, the square of the hypotenuse is the sum of the squares of the other two sides.

$$|AC|^2 = |AB|^2 + |BC|^2$$

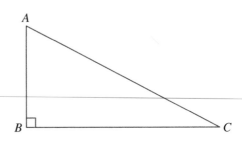

Theorem 15: **Converse to Pythagoras**
If the square of one side is the sum of the squares of the other two, then the angle opposite the first side is a right angle.

Theorem 16: **Area**
For a triangle, base × height does not depend on the choice of base.

Definition:
The area of a triangle is half the base by the height, regardless of which side you choose as the base.

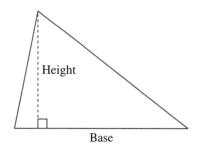

Theorem 17: **Parallelogram bisector**
A diagonal of a parallelogram bisects the area.

$$\text{Area} \triangle ABD = \text{Area} \triangle CDB$$

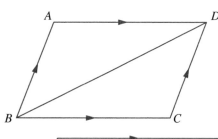

Theorem 18: **Area of a parallelogram**
The area of a parallelogram is the base × height.

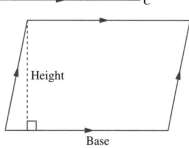

Theorem 19: **Circle theorem**
The angle at the centre of a circle standing on a given arc is twice the angle at any point of the circle standing on the same arc.

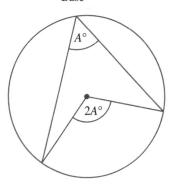

Corollary 1: All angles at points of a circle standing on the same arc are equal.

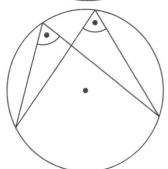

Corollary 2: Each angle in a semicircle is a right angle.

Corollary 3: If the angle standing on a chord $[BC]$ at some point on the circle is a right angle, then $[BC]$ is a diameter.

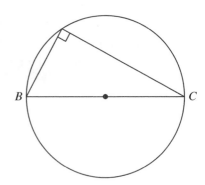

Corollary 4: If $ABCD$ is a cyclic quadrilateral, then opposite angles sum to 180°.

$$A° + C° = 180°$$
$$B° + D° = 180°$$

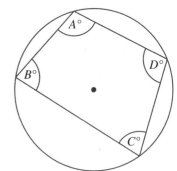

Converse:
If the opposite angles of a quadrilateral sum to 180°, the quadrilateral is cyclic.

Theorem 20: Tangents
1. Each tangent is perpendicular to the radius that goes to the point of contact.
2. If P lies on the circle S, and a line l is perpendicular to the radius at P, then l is a tangent to S.

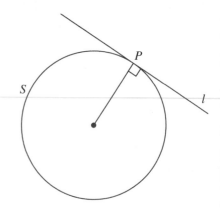

Corollary: If two circles intersect at one point only, then the two centres and the point of contact are collinear.

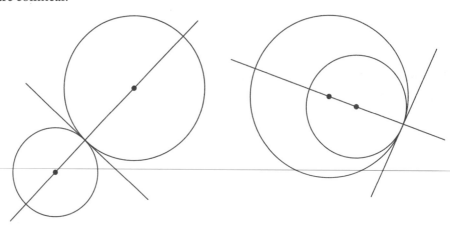

Theorem 21: **Perpendicular bisector of a chord**

1. The perpendicular from the centre of a circle to a chord bisects the chord.
2. The perpendicular bisector of a chord passes through the centre of the circle.

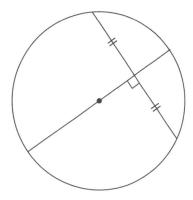

When solving questions that involve diagrams, it is often helpful to do rough copies of the diagram onto a separate piece of paper. This allows you to mark things on the diagram and try different approaches, **without drawing on the original image**. This can be useful if you take the wrong approach the first time. You still have a clean diagram to work from.

Application and use of theorems

You must know all of the theorems, corollaries and axioms very well and be able to apply them when solving geometric problems.

- Be aware that there may be more than one method of proof for answering questions by the application of theorems.
- Many geometry problems will involve aspects of trigonometry.

It is important to give reasons and explanations for statements made when working on a solution in Geometry. This shows that you understand the steps you are taking and will help ensure that you get maximum marks in a question.

(2015 Q.4 (a))

The diagram shows a parallelogram with one side produced.

Use the data on the diagram to find the value of *x*, of *y*, and of *z*. Give a reason for your answer in each case.

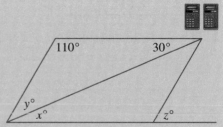

Solution

$x = 30°$	(alternate angles)
$110° + 30° + y = 180°$	(three angles of a triangle sum to 180°)
$140° + y = 180°$	
$y = 40°$	(subtract 140° from both sides)
Angle beside z is 110°	(opposite angles in a parallelogram are equal)
$z + 110° = 180°$	(straight angle)
$z = 70°$	(subtract 110° from both sides)

Example

In the diagram,

$|AB| = |BC|$ and $|AD| = |AC| = |CD|$.

Find:

(i) $|\angle BAC|$
(ii) $|\angle ADC|$
(iii) $|\angle BAD|$

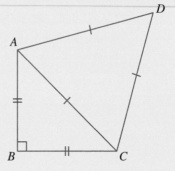

Solution

(i) In $\triangle ABC$:

$$|\angle ABC| + |\angle BAC| + |\angle BCA| = 180° \quad \text{(three angles of a triangle sum to 180°)}$$
$$90° + |\angle BAC| + |\angle BCA| = 180°$$
$$|\angle BAC| + |\angle BCA| = 90°$$

But $|\angle BAC| = |\angle BCA|$ ($\triangle ABC$ is isosceles)

$\therefore |\angle BAC| = 45°$

(ii) Since $\triangle ADC$ is equilateral, the three angles are $60°$ each.

$\therefore |\angle ADC| = 60°$

(iii) $\quad |\angle BAD| = |\angle BAC| + |\angle CAD|$

$\quad |\angle BAD| = 45° + 60°$

$\therefore |\angle BAD| = 105°$

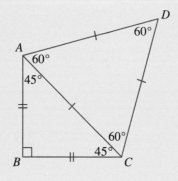

key point

The above example is a very significant question in that initially you are given no numbers whatsoever and yet each angle has a unique exact whole number size.

Example

In the diagram, the line l is a tangent to the circle, where O is the centre.

Find the values of $x°$, $y°$ and $z°$.

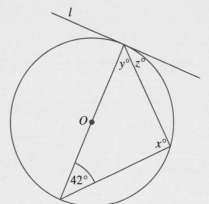

Solution

$$x° = 90° \quad \text{(angle in a semicircle is a right angle)}$$

$$x° + y° + 42° = 180° \quad \text{(three angles of a triangle add up to } 180°)$$

$$90° + y° + 42° = 180°$$

$$y° + 132° = 180°$$

$$y° = 48°$$

$y° + z° = 90°$ (a tangent is perpendicular to the radius at the point of contact)

$48° + z° = 90°$

$z° = 90° − 48°$

$z° = 42°$

Example

C is the centre of the circle k. $[AB]$ and $[XY]$ are diameters of k.

(i) Name another line segment equal in length to $[AC]$. Give a reason for your answer.

(ii) Prove that $\triangle ACX$ and $\triangle BCY$ are congruent.

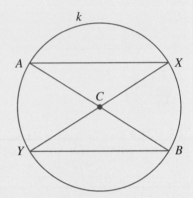

Solution

(i) $[CX]$, $[CY]$ or $[CB]$ are equal in length to the line segment $[AC]$. All of these line segments are radii of the circle k.

(ii) Look at $\triangle ACX$ and $\triangle BCY$:

$|AC| = |CB|$ (both radii)

$|CX| = |CY|$ (both radii)

$|\angle ACX| = |\angle BCY|$ (vertically opposite angles)

$\therefore \triangle ACX \equiv \triangle BCY$ (SAS rule)

key point

It is vital that you are familiar with the rules for congruency:

SAS, ASA, SSS, RHS.

exam Q

(2016 Q.6 (b))

State which one of the following triangles **cannot** be constructed. Give a reason to support your answer.

Triangle 1	Triangle 2
Sides of length (cm) 3·2, 2·9, 5·4	Sides of length (cm) 6, 7, 15

Solution

The triangle inequality states that a triangle can only exist if the sum of any two sides is greater than the third side.

Triangle 1	Triangle 2
$3 \cdot 2 + 2 \cdot 9 > 5 \cdot 4$	$6 + 7 < 15$
$3 \cdot 2 + 5 \cdot 4 > 2 \cdot 9$	$6 + 15 > 7$
$2 \cdot 9 + 5 \cdot 4 > 3 \cdot 2$	$7 + 15 > 6$

Therefore, triangle 1 can be constructed.

Since $6 + 7 < 15$, triangle 2 cannot be constructed.

Example

The lines a, b and c are parallel lines. They cut equal intercepts on the transversal, p.

Calculate the value of the variables x and y.

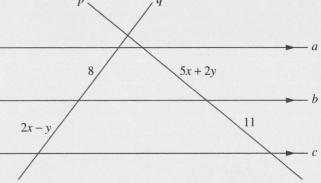

This solution requires the use of simultaneous equations.
Notice the link to algebra.

Solution

From theorem 11, if three parallel lines cut off equal segments on some transversal line, then they will cut off equal segments on any other transversal. Thus, we can say:

The segments on p are equal, therefore $5x + 2y = 11$.

The segments on q are equal, therefore $2x - y = 8$.

Solve for x and y, using simultaneous equations:

		Now solve for y:	
$5x + 2y = 11$		$5x + 2y = 11$	
$2x - y = 8$	(multiply by 2)	$5(3) + 2y = 11$	(sub in value for x)
$5x + 2y = 11$		$15 + 2y = 11$	
$4x - 2y = 16$	(add the rows)	$2y = -4$	
$9x = 27$		$y = -2$	
$x = 3$			

'If a number is divisible by 8, it is also divisible by 4.'

(i) What is the converse of this statement?

(ii) Is the converse true? Give an example to explain your answer.

Solution

(i) The converse is 'if a number is divisible by 4, then it is also divisible by 8'.

(ii) This converse is not true. For example, 20 is divisible by 4 but it is not divisible by 8.

(i) In $\triangle STR$, $XY \parallel ST$. Explain why $\triangle STR$ and $\triangle XYR$ are similar.

(ii) $|SX| = 4$ cm, $|RY| = 10$ cm and $|SR| = 12$ cm. Calculate $|XR|$.

(iii) Calculate $|TR|$.

(iv) Calculate $|YT|$.

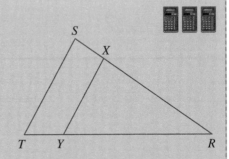

Similar triangles are triangles in which all corresponding angles are equal. They can also be called equiangular triangles.

Solution

(i) Redraw $\triangle STR$ and $\triangle XYR$ separately.

Label angles 1, 2, 3, 4, 5 and 6, as in the diagram below.

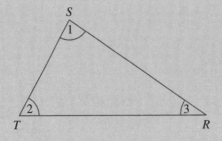

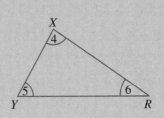

$ST \parallel XY$, therefore, $|\angle 1| = |\angle 4|$ and $|\angle 2| = |\angle 5|$.   (corresponding angles)

$\therefore \triangle STR$ and $\triangle XYR$ are similar.   (any two pairs of matching angles)

Labelling the angles of a triangle with letters or numbers can help to simplify a solution.

key point

You only need to show that two of the three pairs of matching angles are equal to prove that two triangles are similar.

(ii) Redraw the shape, filling in any known sides. Looking at [SR], we can see that:

$$|SR| = |SX| + |XR|$$
$$12 = 4 + |XR|$$
$$\therefore 8 \text{ cm} = |XR|$$

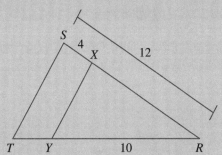

(iii) Redraw △STR and △XYR separately and fill in all known sides.

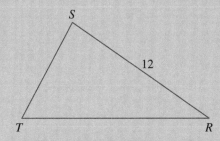

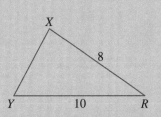

Analyse the corresponding sides.
Take two pairs of corresponding sides:

$$\frac{|TR|}{|YR|} = \frac{|SR|}{|XR|}$$

$$\frac{|TR|}{10} = \frac{12}{8}$$

△STR	△XYR
|SR| = 12	|XR| = 8
|TR| = ?	|YR| = 10
|ST| = ?	|XY| = ?

$$|TR| = \frac{12 \times 10}{8}$$ (multiply both sides by 10)

$$|TR| = \frac{120}{8}$$

$$|TR| = 15 \text{ cm}$$

key point

Put the unknown side on the top of the fraction, on LHS.

(iv) Looking at $[TR]$:

$$|TY| + |YR| = |TR|$$

$$|TY| + 10 = 15$$

$$\therefore \quad |TY| = 5 \text{ cm}$$

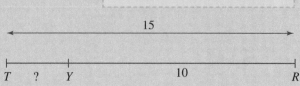

exam Q

(2012 Q.6B)

ABCD is a parallelogram.

The points *A*, *B* and *C* lie on the circle, which cuts $[AD]$ at *P*.

The line *CP* meets the line *BA* at *Q*.

Prove that $|CD| = |CP|$.

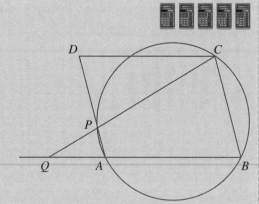

Solution

To prove $|CD| = |CP|$, we must prove $\triangle CDP$ is isosceles.

Label the angles 1, 2, 3 and 4.

$|\angle 1| = |\angle 4|$ (opposite angles of a parallelogram)

$|\angle 3| + |\angle 4| = 180°$ (opposite angles of a cyclic quadrilateral)

$|\angle 2| + |\angle 3| = 180°$ (straight angle)

$\therefore |\angle 3| + |\angle 4| = |\angle 2| + |\angle 3|$

$\therefore |\angle 4| = |\angle 2|$

$\therefore |\angle 1| = |\angle 2|$ (since $|\angle 1| = |\angle 4|$)

$\therefore \triangle CDP$ is isosceles

$\therefore |CD| = |CP|$

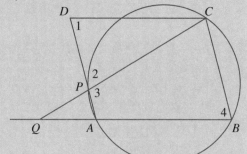

exam focus

This question was poorly answered. It was worth 25 marks: 8 of these marks were awarded for any correct step and 17 marks awarded for a correct conclusion with one or two steps incorrect or missing.

QR and *QP* are both tangents to circle *c* with centre *O*.

(i) If $|\angle PSR| = 57°$, find *x*.

(ii) Prove that $|QR| = |QP|$.

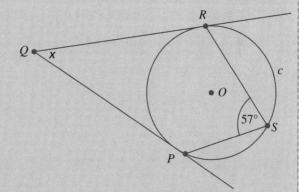

Solution

(i) Construct the radii *OR* and *OP*.

$|\angle ORQ| = 90°$ (*RQ* is a tangent)

$|\angle OPQ| = 90°$ (*PQ* is a tangent)

$|\angle ROP| = 114°$ ($|\angle ROP| = 2|\angle RSP|$, since the angle at the centre is twice the angle at the circle standing on the same arc)

$|\angle ORQ| + |\angle OPQ| + |\angle PQR| + |\angle ROP| = 360°$

(4 angles of a quadrilateral)

$$90° + 90° + x + 114° = 360°$$

$$x = 66°$$

(ii) To prove $|QR| = |QP|$, we must prove $\triangle QRO$ and $\triangle QPO$ are congruent.

Construct the line OQ.

$|OR| = |OP|$	(both radii)
$|OQ| = |OQ|$	(common line)
$|\angle ORQ| = |\angle OPQ|$	(both 90°)
$\therefore \triangle QRO \equiv \triangle QPO$	(RHS)
$\therefore |QR| = |QP|$	

key point

You could also have proven $|QR| = |QP|$ by showing that $\triangle PQR$ is isosceles.

---

exam Q

(2014 Q.6B)

Two circles c_1 and c_2, intersect at the points B and X, as shown. The circle c_1, has diameter $[AB]$. The circle c_2, has diameter $[BC]$. The line CB is a tangent to c_1.

Prove that X is on the line AC.

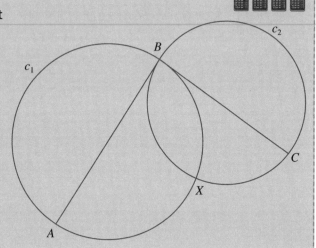

Solution

Since [AB] is a diameter of c_1, $|\angle AXB| = 90°$, since the angle in a semicircle is a right-angle.

Since [BC] is a diameter of c_2, $|\angle CXB| = 90°$, since the angle in a semicircle is a right-angle.

Therefore $|\angle AXC| = 180°$.

So the points A, X and C are on a straight line.

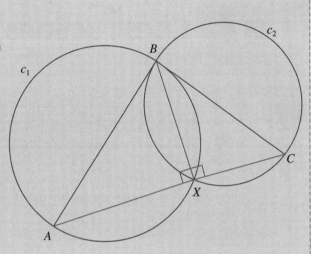

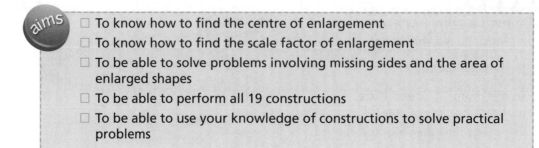

4 Enlargements and Constructions

aims

- ☐ To know how to find the centre of enlargement
- ☐ To know how to find the scale factor of enlargement
- ☐ To be able to solve problems involving missing sides and the area of enlarged shapes
- ☐ To be able to perform all 19 constructions
- ☐ To be able to use your knowledge of constructions to solve practical problems

Enlargements

An **enlargement** changes the size of a shape to give a similar image. To enlarge a shape, we need:

1. A centre of enlargement   **2.** A scale factor.

When a shape is enlarged, all lengths are multiplied by the scale factor and all angles remain unchanged. A slide projector makes an enlargement of a shape. In this case, the light bulb is the **centre of enlargement**.

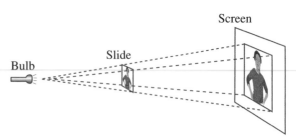

Ray method

In the diagram below, the triangle ABC is the **object** (the starting shape) and the triangle $A'B'C'$ is the **image** (the enlarged shape) under an enlargement, centre O and a scale factor of $\frac{1}{2}$.

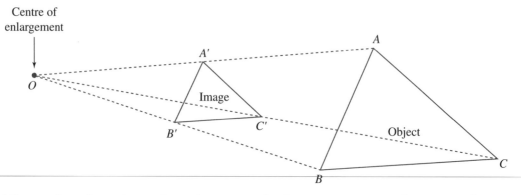

The rays have been drawn from the centre of enlargement, O, to each vertex and beyond. The distance from the centre of enlargement, O, to each vertex on triangle ABC was measured and multiplied by $\frac{1}{2}$. Thus, $|OA'| = \frac{1}{2}|OA|, |OB'| = \frac{1}{2}|OB|$ and $|OC'| = \frac{1}{2}|OC|$.

Also, $|A'B'| = \frac{1}{2}|AB|, |A'C'| = \frac{1}{2}|AC|$ and $|B'C'| = \frac{1}{2}|BC|$.

Note: All measurements are made from the centre of enlargement, O.

Properties of enlargements:

1. The shape of the image is the same as the shape of the object (only the size has changed).
2. The amount by which a figure is enlarged is called the **scale factor** and is denoted by k.
3. Image length = k(object length)   or $k = \dfrac{\text{Image length}}{\text{Object length}}$
4. Area of image = k^2(area of object)   or $k^2 = \dfrac{\text{Area of image}}{\text{Area of object}}$

1. The scale factor can be less than 1 (i.e. $0 < k < 1$). In these cases, the image will be smaller than the object. Though smaller, the image is still called an enlargement.

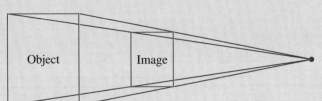

2. The centre of enlargement can be a vertex on the object figure.

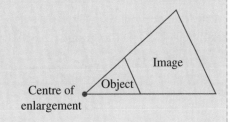

To find the centre of enlargement, do the following:

1. Choose two points on the image and their corresponding points on the original figure.
2. From each of these points on the larger figure, draw a line to the corresponding point on the smaller figure.
3. Produce these lines until they intersect at the point that is the centre of enlargement.

exam Q

Construct the enlargement of triangle *ABC*, with centre of enlargement *O* and a scale factor of 3.

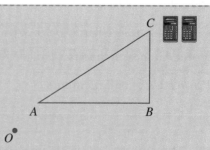

Solution

To form an image of △*ABC* with a scale factor of 3:

1. Draw rays from the point *O* through each of the points *A*, *B* and *C*.
2. Measure how far point *A* is from *O* and then construct the point *A′* a distance of 3 times away from *O*, along the ray passing through the point *A*.
3. Measure how far point *B* is from *O* and then construct the point *B′* a distance of 3 times away from *O*, along the ray passing through the point *B*.
4. Measure how far point *C* is from *O* and then construct the point *C′* a distance of 3 times away from *O*, along the ray passing through the point *C*.

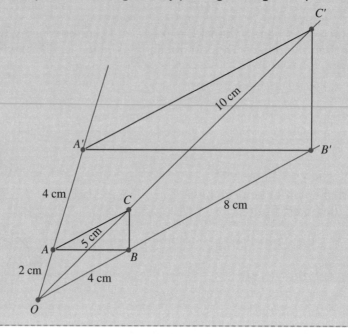

exam focus

Sometimes you will meet words you have never heard before, like 'pantograph' in the next example. If this happens, don't panic! Look for the information that you need to solve the question and don't worry about the complicated language.

Example

A pantograph is a drawing tool which can be used to reduce or enlarge
an image by hand. A graphic designer is using a pantograph to enlarge
the Gill logo.

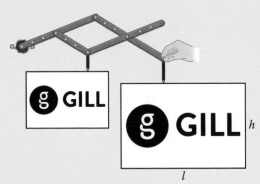

The original logo is 3 cm long and 2 cm high.
He sets the pantograph to enlarge by a scale factor, k, of 1·5.

(i) Find the length l of the enlarged image.

(ii) Find the height h of the enlarged image.

(iii) Hence, find the area of the enlarged image.

(iv) Calculate $\dfrac{\text{Area of enlarged image}}{\text{Area of original image}}$ and verify that this equals k^2.

Solution

(i) Image height = k (object height)
Image length = 1·5 (3)
Image length = 4·5 cm

(ii) Image height = k (object height)
Image height = 1·5 (2)
Image height = 3 cm

(iii)

4·5 cm

3 cm **g GILL**

Area = length × height
Area = 4·5 × 3
Area = 13·5 cm²

(iv) $\dfrac{\text{Area of enlarged image}}{\text{Area of original image}} = \dfrac{13\cdot5}{6} = 2\cdot25$

$k^2 = (1\cdot5)^2 = 2\cdot25$

$\therefore \dfrac{\text{Area of enlarged image}}{\text{Area of original image}} = k^2$

Triangle *PQR* is the image of triangle *ABC* under an enlargement.

$|PR| = 8$ cm, $|AC| = 4$ cm,

$|AB| = 3$ cm and $|QR| = 4$ cm.

(i) Write down the centre of enlargement.

(ii) Find the scale factor, *k*.

(iii) Find **(a)** $|PQ|$ **(b)** $|BC|$.

(iv) If the area of triangle *ABC* is 2·9 cm², find the area of triangle *PQR*.

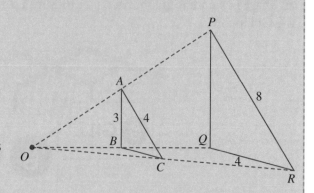

Solution

(i) Write down the centre of enlargement:

The centre of enlargement is the point *O*, as this is the point where the three lines joining the corresponding corners intersect.

(ii) Find the scale factor, *k*.

$$k = \frac{\text{Image length}}{\text{Object length}}$$

$$k = \frac{|PR|}{|AC|} = \frac{8}{4}$$

$$k = 2$$

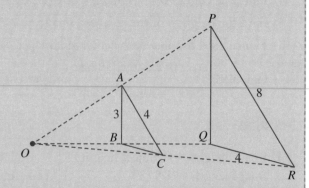

(iii) Find **(a)** $|PQ|$ **(b)** $|BC|$.

(a) $k = \dfrac{\text{Image length}}{\text{Object length}}$

$$k = \frac{|PQ|}{|AB|}$$

$$2 = \frac{|PQ|}{3}$$

$$6 \text{ cm} = |PQ|$$

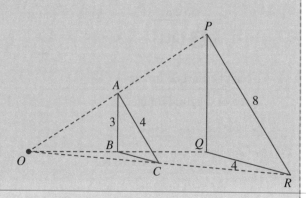

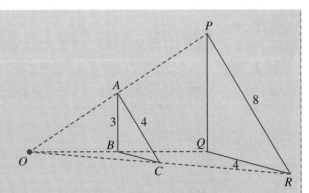

(b) $k = \dfrac{\text{Image length}}{\text{Object length}}$

$k = \dfrac{|QR|}{|BC|}$

$2 = \dfrac{4}{|BC|}$

$2|BC| = 4$

$|BC| = 2 \text{ cm}$

(iv) If the area of triangle ABC is $2 \cdot 9$ cm², find the area of triangle PQR.

$k^2 = \dfrac{\text{Area of image}}{\text{Area of object}}$

$2^2 = \dfrac{\text{Area of } \triangle PQR}{2 \cdot 9}$

$4 = \dfrac{\text{Area of } \triangle PQR}{2 \cdot 9}$ (multiply both sides by 2·9)

$11 \cdot 6 \text{ cm}^2 = \text{Area of } \triangle PQR$

A necklace is made with beads which are identical in shape, but different sizes.

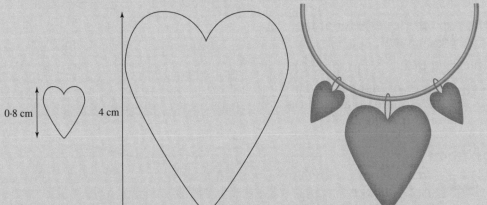

The height of the smaller bead is 0·8 cm and its area is 0·6 cm². The height of the larger bead is 4 cm.

Find the area of the larger bead.

Solution

Need to find the scale factor of enlargement:

$$k = \frac{\text{Image height}}{\text{Object height}}$$

$$k = \frac{4}{0 \cdot 8}$$

$$k = 5$$

$$k^2 = \frac{\text{Area of image}}{\text{Area of object}}$$

$$5^2 = \frac{\text{Area of image}}{0 \cdot 6}$$

$$25 = \frac{\text{Area of image}}{0 \cdot 6} \quad (\times 0 \cdot 6)$$

$$25(0 \cdot 6) = \text{Area of image}$$

$$15 \text{ cm}^2 = \text{Area of image}$$

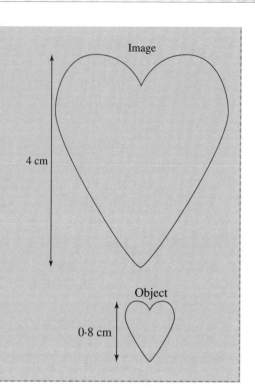

Image

4 cm

0·8 cm

Object

exam Q

Triangle *OXY* is the image of triangle *OAB* under the enlargement, centre *O*, with $|XY| = 8$, $|OX| = 10$ and $|AB| = 18$.

(i) Find the scale factor of the enlargement.

(ii) Find $|XA|$.

(iii) The area of triangle *OAB* is 101·25 square units. Find the area of triangle *OXY*.

 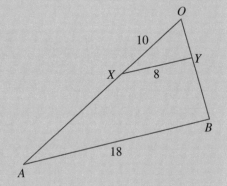

Solution

(i) $k = \dfrac{\text{Image length}}{\text{Object length}} = \dfrac{|XY|}{|AB|}$

$k = \dfrac{8}{18} = \dfrac{4}{9}$

(ii)

$$k = \frac{\text{Image length}}{\text{Object length}} = \frac{|OX|}{|OA|}$$

$$\frac{4}{9} = \frac{10}{|OA|}$$

$$4|OA| = 9(10)$$

$$|OA| = \frac{90}{4} = 22 \cdot 5$$

$$|OA| = |OX| + |AX|$$

$$22 \cdot 5 = 10 + |AX|$$

$$12 \cdot 5 = |AX|$$

(iii) The area of triangle OAB is 101·25 square units. Find the area of triangle OXY.

$$k^2 = \frac{\text{Area of image}}{\text{Area of object}}$$

$$\left(\frac{4}{9}\right)^2 = \frac{\text{Area of image}}{101 \cdot 25}$$

$$\frac{16}{81} = \frac{\text{Area of image}}{101 \cdot 25}$$

$$\frac{16(101 \cdot 25)}{81} = \text{Area of image}$$

$$20 = \text{Area of image}$$

key point

In the last question, the enlargement of *OAB* resulted in a smaller triangle. It is important for you to be aware that an enlargement does not mean to get bigger.

Constructions

There are 19 constructions on the Leaving Cert Ordinary Level course. Please note that, in the table below, the numbering of these constructions are as outlined in the syllabus. Constructions 3 and 7 are not listed, as they are not required for the Leaving Certificate Ordinary Level Maths course.

1. Bisector of an angle, using only a compass and straight edge
2. Perpendicular bisector of a segment, using only a compass and straight edge
4. Line perpendicular to a given line *l*, passing through a given point on *l*
5. Line parallel to given line, through a given point
6. Division of a line segment into two or three equal segments without measuring it
8. Line segment of a given length on a given ray
9. Angle of a given number of degrees with a given ray as one arm
10. Triangle, given length of three sides (SSS)
11. Triangle, given two sides and the included angle (SAS)
12. Triangle, given two angles and the common side (ASA)
13. Right-angled triangle, given length of hypotenuse and one other side (RHS)
14. Right-angled triangle, given one side and one of the acute angles
15. Rectangle, given side lengths

16. Circumcentre and circumcircle of a given triangle, using only a straight edge and compass
17. Incentre and incircle of a given triangle, using only a straight edge and compass
18. Angle of 60° without using a protractor or set square
19. Tangent to a given circle at a given point on it
20. Parallelogram, given the length of the sides and the measure of the angles
21. Centroid of a triangle

- The steps required for completing each of these constructions are detailed in your textbook.
- Computer simulations of these constructions can be found at www.mathopenref.com.
- Any work involving accurate constructions requires a good pencil, eraser, a compass, a ruler, a set square and a protractor.

There is a theorem on your Geometry course that can be used to construct the tangent to a circle at a given point on the circle.

State this theorem and use it to construct the tangent to a circle at a point *P*.

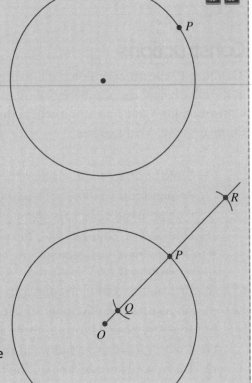

Solution

Theorem: Each tangent is perpendicular to the radius that goes to the point of contact.

Construction

1. Draw a line from the centre, through *P*, and beyond the circle.

2. With the compass point on *P*, draw an arc on each side of *P*, an equal distance away, creating *Q* and *R*.

3. With the compass point on *Q*, set its width to a length greater than |*QP*|. Keep the compass on *Q* and draw an arc to the left of *P*.

4. Without changing the compass width, repeat for point *R*, creating point *S*.

5. Draw a line through *P* and *S*.

   The line *PS* is the tangent to the circle at *P*.

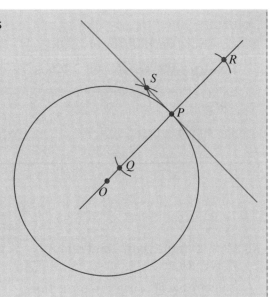

It is important to show **all** construction lines or marks you make at any stage during the construction. Erasing any of these may result in marks being lost in an exam.

exam Q

(i) Construct the incentre of the triangle *ABC* using only a compass and straight edge. Show all construction lines clearly.

(ii) Hence, construct the incircle of triangle *ABC*.

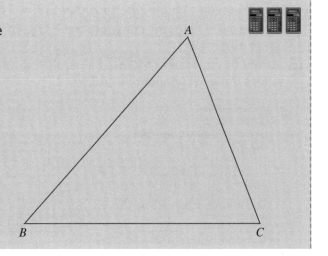

Solution

(i) Construct the bisector of ∠ABC.

Construct the bisector of ∠ACB.

Extend these bisectors to meet at the point K.

K is the incentre.

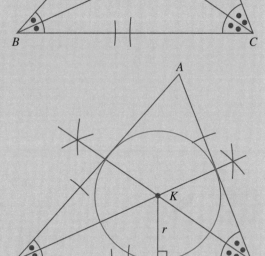

(ii) With K as the centre and radius r, draw a circle.

This circle will touch the three sides of the triangle.

The circle drawn is the incircle.

(2013 Q.6A)

(a) Construct the triangle ABC such that |AB| = 8 cm, |BC| = |AC| = 5 cm.

(b) On the same diagram, construct the image of the triangle ABC under the axial symmetry in AB.

(c) Justify the statement 'AC'BC is a parallelogram' where C' is the image of C under the axial symmetry in AB.

Solution

(a) • Draw the base line [AB], 8 cm long.

• Draw arcs of length 5 cm from each of the points A and B.

• These arcs intersect at the point C.

• Join the points A, B and C to construct the triangle.

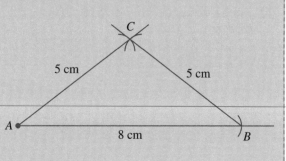

(b) Construct the image of the triangle in axial symmetry in the line [AB]:

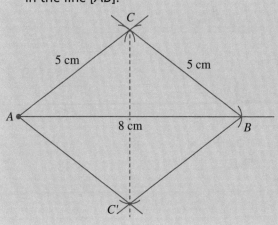

(c) From the image, we can see:

The opposite sides of AC'BC are equal.

The diagonals of AC'BC bisect each other.

The opposite angles in AC'BC are equal.

Therefore, AC'BC is a parallelogram.

exam
Q

The diagram shows an island. There is treasure buried at the point T.
T is equidistant from A and B and is also equidistant from C and D.

Using only a compass and straight edge, locate the point T.

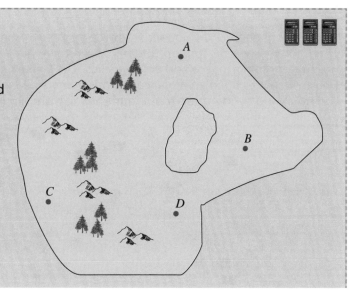

Solution

Any point along the perpendicular bisector of a line segment is equidistant from the two ends of the line segment.

Construct the perpendicular bisector of [*AB*] and the perpendicular bisector of [*CD*].

The point where these bisectors intersect is *T*.

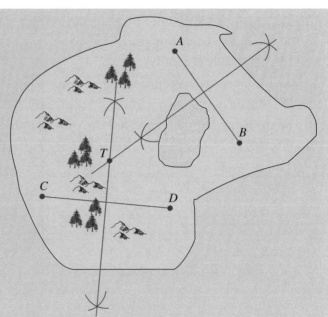

Cavan, Monaghan and Dundalk are three large towns in Ireland. These towns are indicated on the map. Each town has a local hospital for minor needs and emergencies. The Department of Health wants to build an advanced, modern medical facility, which can be shared by the three towns and their surrounding communities.

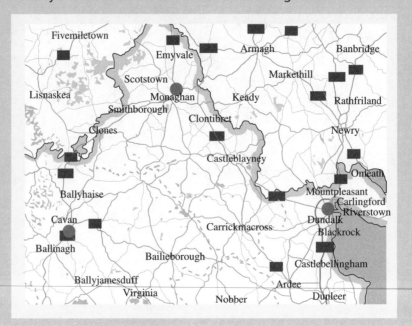

You have been asked to determine the best location for this facility.

(i) What do you think is the most important issue when deciding the location of the new medical facility?

(ii) Accurately construct the most appropriate position of the new medical facility.

(iii) By studying the map, do you think this location is the best place for the new medical facility? Give a reason for your answer.

Solution

(i) The medical facility should be equidistant (the same distance) from each of the three towns.

(ii) The point which is equidistant from each of the towns is known as the circumcentre.

To construct the circumcentre:

1. Join the towns to form a triangle.

2. Label the points C, M and D.

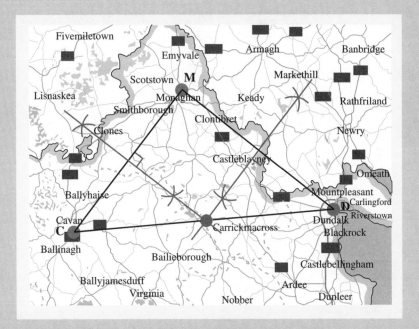

3. Construct the perpendicular bisectors of [CM] and [MD].

4. The point where these bisectors intersect is the circumcentre of the triangle.

The new medical facility should be placed at the circumcentre, which is indicated by a large blue dot on the map.

(iii) No, I do not think the location of the circumcentre is the best place for the new medical centre, as it is away from the main roads. It may be better to place the medical facility slightly closer to some main roads. Even though it will be physically further away from one town than the others, it may make it quicker to access.

Also, one of the towns may have a much bigger population than the others, so it may be wiser to place the medical facility closer to that town.

OR

Yes, I think the location of the circumcentre is the best place for the new medical centre, as it is an equal distance from each of the towns, so it is the fairest place to put it.

In the exam, when you are asked for your opinion you must be aware that more than one answer can be valid. Whatever opinion you give, it is important that you give reasons to back up your opinion.

aims
- ☐ To learn how to solve triangles to find missing sides or angles
- ☐ To learn how to find the area of a triangle
- ☐ To learn how to find the area and perimeter of a sector of a circle
- ☐ To learn how to solve trigonometric equations

Trigonometric formulae

Formulae for right-angled triangles only

Pythagoras's theorem:

$$c^2 = a^2 + b^2$$

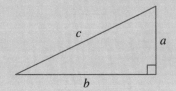

(see *booklet of formulae and tables*, page 16)

The three trigonometric ratios for a right-angled triangle, $0° < \theta < 90°$, are:

$$\sin \theta = \frac{O}{H}$$

$$\cos \theta = \frac{A}{H}$$

$$\tan \theta = \frac{O}{A}$$

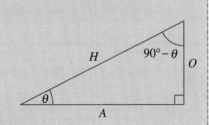

From the diagram, we can see that:

$$\sin(90° - \theta) = \frac{A}{H} = \cos \theta \quad \text{and} \quad \cos(90° - \theta) = \frac{O}{H} = \sin \theta$$

(similar diagram in *booklet of formulae and tables*, page 16)

key point

These ratios hold for all values of $\theta \in \mathbb{R}$, not just for $0° < \theta < 90°$.

Formulae for all triangles

Sine rule

$$\frac{a}{\sin A} = \frac{b}{\sin B} = \frac{c}{\sin C}$$

or

$$\frac{\sin A}{a} = \frac{\sin B}{b} = \frac{\sin C}{c}$$

Cosine rule

$$a^2 = b^2 + c^2 - 2bc \cos A \quad \boxed{or} \quad b^2 = a^2 + c^2 - 2ac \cos B \quad \boxed{or} \quad c^2 = a^2 + b^2 - 2ab \cos C$$

Rearrange to find the angle:

$$\cos A = \frac{b^2 + c^2 - a^2}{2bc} \quad \boxed{or} \quad \cos B = \frac{a^2 + c^2 - b^2}{2ac} \quad \boxed{or} \quad \cos C = \frac{a^2 + b^2 - c^2}{2ab}$$

(see *booklet of formulae and tables*, page 16)

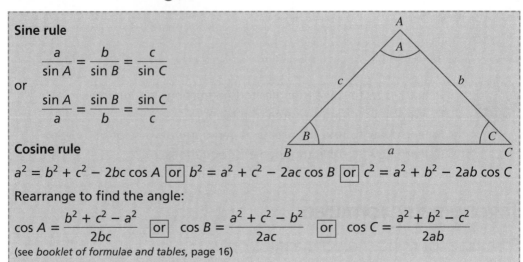

key point

- When using the **sine rule**, always place the unknown quantity on the top of the left fraction.
- If you need to use the **cosine rule** to find an angle, rearrange the rule first, then substitute the known values. This means that you can enter the solution directly into a calculator.

Use the following flowchart to work out which formula to use:

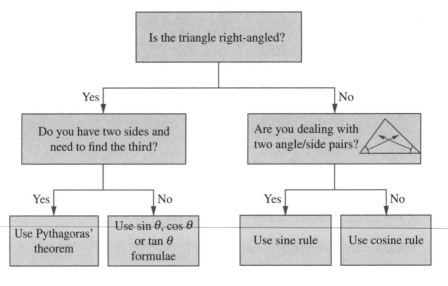

The cosine rule must be used, in a non-right-angled triangle, if:

You are given the three sides and need to find an angle.

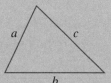

OR

You are given two sides and the included angle and need to find the third side.

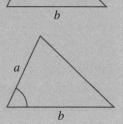

(2016 Q.6 (c))

The lengths of the sides of a right-angled triangle are 5, x, and $x + 1$ as shown.

Use the Theorem of Pythagoras to find the value of x.

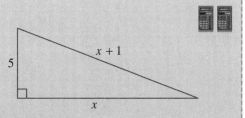

Solution

$$c^2 = a^2 + b^2$$
$$(x + 1)^2 = (x)^2 + (5)^2$$
$$x^2 + 2x + 1 = x^2 + 25 \quad \text{(expand brackets)}$$
$$2x + 1 = 25 \quad \text{(subtract } x^2 \text{ from both sides)}$$
$$2x = 24 \quad \text{(subtract 1 from both sides)}$$
$$x = 12 \quad \text{(divide both sides by 2)}$$

Example

(i) Find $|\angle CAD|$.

(ii) Find $|AC|$, correct to one decimal place.

(iii) Find $|AB|$.

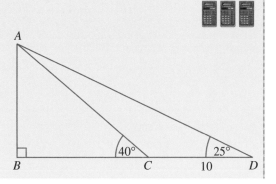

Solution

(i) The angle at C is a straight angle, so it measures $180°$.

$\therefore |\angle ACD| = 180° - 40°$

$\therefore |\angle ACD| = 140°$

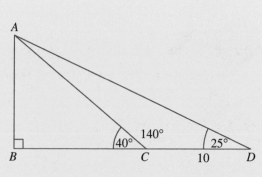

$\triangle ACD$: The three angles sum to $180°$.

$\therefore |\angle CAD| = 180° - 140° - 25°$

$\therefore |\angle CAD| = 15°$

(ii) On $\triangle ACD$:

Using the flowchart on page 72, we can see that we use the sine rule.

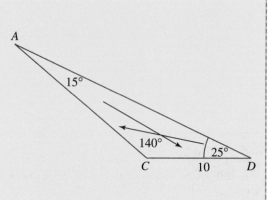

$$\frac{|AC|}{\sin|\angle ADC|} = \frac{|CD|}{\sin|\angle CAD|}$$

$$\frac{|AC|}{\sin 25°} = \frac{10}{\sin 15°}$$

$$|AC| = \frac{10 \sin 25°}{\sin 15°}$$

$$|AC| = 16.328$$

$$|AC| = 16.3 \qquad \text{(correct to one decimal place)}$$

(iii) In $\triangle ABC$, find $|AB|$.

$$\sin A = \frac{\text{opp}}{\text{hyp}}$$

$$\sin 40° = \frac{|AB|}{16.3}$$

$$16.3 \sin 40° = |AB|$$

$$10.477 = |AB|$$

$$10.5 = |AB| \qquad \text{(correct to one decimal place)}$$

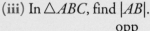

Example

If $\tan A = \dfrac{1}{3}$, find the value of $\sin^2 A + \cos^2 A$.

Solution

$$\tan A = \frac{1}{3} = \frac{\text{opp}}{\text{adj}}$$

Construct the triangle with angle A, where opposite $= 1$ and adjacent $= 3$.

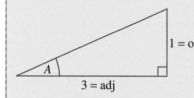

Use Pythagoras's theorem to find the third side:

$$(\text{hyp})^2 = (\text{opp})^2 + (\text{adj})^2$$
$$(\text{hyp})^2 = (1)^2 + (3)^2$$
$$(\text{hyp})^2 = 1 + 9$$
$$(\text{hyp})^2 = 10$$
$$\text{hyp} = \sqrt{10}$$

$$\sin A = \frac{\text{opp}}{\text{hyp}} \Rightarrow \sin A = \frac{1}{\sqrt{10}}$$

$$\cos A = \frac{\text{adj}}{\text{hyp}} \Rightarrow \cos A = \frac{3}{\sqrt{10}}$$

$$\sin^2 A + \cos^2 A = \left(\frac{1}{\sqrt{10}}\right)^2 + \left(\frac{3}{\sqrt{10}}\right)^2$$

$$\sin^2 A + \cos^2 A = \frac{1}{10} + \frac{9}{10}$$

$$\sin^2 A + \cos^2 A = \frac{10}{10}$$

$$\sin^2 A + \cos^2 A = 1$$

exam Q

In the diagram, $|PQ| = 4$ cm, $|PR| = 5$ cm, $|QR| = 6$ cm and $|\angle PSR| = 22°$.

Find $|PS|$.

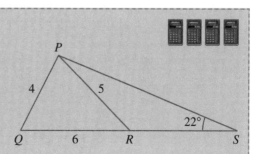

Solution

Two triangles are linked and we need to work on them separately to find $|PS|$.

1. $\triangle PQR$

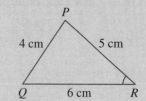

Let $p = |QR|$
$q = |PR|$
$r = |PQ|$
and $R = |\angle QRP|$.

We use the cosine rule to calculate R.

$$r^2 = q^2 + p^2 - 2qr \cos R$$
$$4^2 = 5^2 + 6^2 - 2(5)(6) \cos R \quad \text{(put in known values)}$$
$$16 = 25 + 36 - 60 \cos R$$
$$60 \cos R = 25 + 36 - 16$$
$$60 \cos R = 45$$
$$\cos R = \frac{45}{60} \quad \text{(divide both sides by 60)}$$
$$\cos R = \frac{3}{4} \quad \left(\frac{45}{60} = \frac{3}{4}\right)$$
$$R = \cos^{-1} \frac{3}{4}$$
$$R = 41 \cdot 40962211$$
$$\therefore |\angle QRP| = 41 \cdot 4° \quad \text{(correct to one decimal place)}$$

Now $|\angle PRS| = 180° - 41 \cdot 4°$
$|\angle PRS| = 138 \cdot 6°$

Labelling the sides of the triangle with letters can make it easier when working with the formula.

2. $\triangle PRS$

We now use the sine rule to find $|PS|$, as we have two angles and one side.

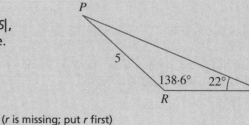

From the diagram, $|PS| = r$.

$$\frac{r}{\sin R} = \frac{s}{\sin S}$$
$$\frac{r}{\sin 138 \cdot 6°} = \frac{5}{\sin 22°} \quad \text{(r is missing; put r first)}$$
$$r = \frac{5 \sin 138 \cdot 6°}{\sin 22°}$$
$$r = 8 \cdot 826751543$$

Thus, $|PS| = 8 \cdot 83$ cm. \quad (correct to two decimal places)

Area of triangles and sectors

Given two sides and the angle in between these sides:

$$\text{Area} = \frac{1}{2}ab\sin C = \frac{1}{2}ac\sin B = \frac{1}{2}bc\sin A$$

Given the three sides:

$$s = \frac{a+b+c}{2}$$

$$\text{Area} = \sqrt{s(s-a)(s-b)(s-c)}$$

(see *booklet of formulae and tables*, page 9)

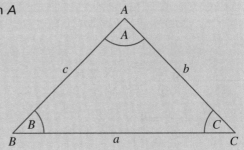

Sectors

Length of arc: $l = 2\pi r\left(\dfrac{\theta}{360°}\right)$

Area of sector: $A = \pi r^2\left(\dfrac{\theta}{360°}\right)$

(see *booklet of formulae and tables*, page 9)

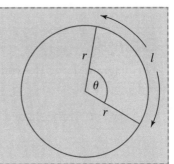

Example

(i) Find the area of a sector of a circle of radius 4 cm if the arc of the sector subtends an angle of 60° at the centre.

(ii) The radius of a circle is 10 cm. Find the angle subtended at the centre by an arc of length 4π cm.

Solution

(i) $r = 4, \theta = 60°$. Find the area.

$$A = \frac{\theta}{360°} \times \pi r^2$$

$$A = \frac{60°}{360°} \times \pi(4)^2$$

$$A = \frac{1}{6} \times \pi(16)$$

$$A = \frac{8}{3}\pi \ \text{cm}^2$$

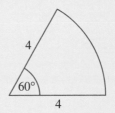

(ii) $r = 10, l = 4\pi$. Find θ.

$$l = \frac{\theta}{360°} \times 2\pi r$$

$$4\pi = \frac{\theta}{360°} \times 2\pi(10)$$

$$4\pi = \frac{\theta}{360°} \times 20\pi \qquad (\times 360)$$

$$1{,}440\pi = \theta \times 20\pi \qquad (\div 20\pi)$$

$$72° = \theta$$

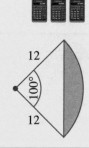

Example

The diagram shows the sector of a circle of radius 12 cm and angle 100°.

Find the area of the shaded region (segment).

Solution

Area of shaded region = Area of sector − Area of triangle

Area of sector $= \dfrac{\theta}{360°} \times \pi r^2$	Area of triangle $= \dfrac{1}{2} ab \sin C$
Area of sector $= \dfrac{100}{360°} \times \pi(12)^2$	Area of triangle $= \dfrac{1}{2}(12)(12) \sin 100°$
Area of sector $= \dfrac{100}{360°} \times 144\pi$	Area of triangle $= (72) \sin 100°$
Area of sector $= 40\pi$	Area of triangle $= 70{\cdot}91$
Area of sector $= 125{\cdot}66$	

Area of shaded region = Area of sector − Area of triangle

Area of shaded region = $125{\cdot}66 - 70{\cdot}91$

Area of shaded region = $54{\cdot}75$ cm^2

Example

In $\triangle PQR$, $|PR| = \sqrt{8}$ m, $|\angle RPQ| = 30°$ and $|\angle PQR| = 45°$.

(i) Find $|QR|$.

(ii) Show that the area of $\triangle PRQ = 2{\cdot}7$ m^2, correct to one decimal place.

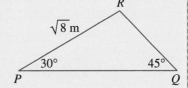

Solution

(i) Use the sine rule to find $|QR|$.

$$\frac{|QR|}{\sin P} = \frac{|PR|}{\sin Q}$$

$$\frac{|QR|}{\sin 30°} = \frac{\sqrt{8}}{\sin 45°}$$

$$|QR| = \frac{\sqrt{8}\,\sin 30°}{\sin 45°}$$

$$|QR| = \frac{2\sqrt{2}\left(\frac{1}{2}\right)}{\frac{1}{\sqrt{2}}}$$

$$|QR| = 2$$

(ii) Area of $\triangle PQR = \frac{1}{2}|PR||QR|\sin R$

We need angle R.

The three angles of the triangle sum to 180°.

$R = 180° - 45° - 30°$

$R = 105°$

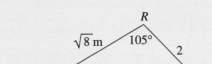

Thus, area $= \frac{1}{2}(\sqrt{8})(2)\sin 105°$

$= 2{\cdot}732050808$

$= 2{\cdot}7$ m^2 (correct to one decimal place)

key point

You can enter the entire $\dfrac{\sqrt{8}\ \sin 30°}{\sin 45°}$ into the calculator as one operation to minimise the chance of errors.

exam Q

(2014 Q.5 (a), (b))

(a) The square $ABCD$ has an area of 81 cm^2. Find $|AD|$.

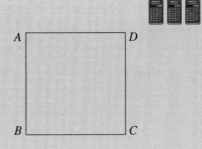

(b) A sector of a circle, centre B and radius |BC|, is drawn inside *ABCD* as shown by the shaded region.

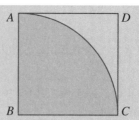

   (i) Find the area of the sector, correct to one decimal place.

   (ii) A second sector of a circle, centre *D* and radius |DA|, is drawn. Find the area of the shaded region (the overlap of the two sectors), correct to one decimal place.

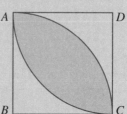

Solution

(a) Area of the square = 81

$$(\text{Length})^2 = 81$$

$$\text{Length} = \sqrt{81} = 9 \text{ cm}$$

(b) (i) Area of sector $= \dfrac{\theta}{360°} \times \pi r^2$

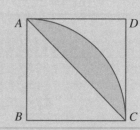

$$= \dfrac{90°}{360°} \times \pi(9)^2 = 63 \cdot 6 \text{ cm}^2$$

   (ii) Half of the shaded region (as shown)

$$= \text{Sector } ABC - \text{Triangle } ABC$$

$$= 63 \cdot 6 - \dfrac{1}{2}(9)(9)$$

$$= 63 \cdot 6 - 40 \cdot 5$$

$$= 23 \cdot 1$$

   Therefore, shaded region = 2(23·1) = 46·2 cm².

Unit circle

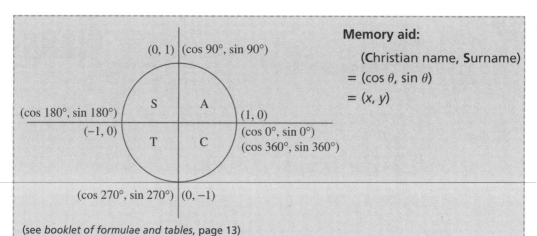

Memory aid:

(**C**hristian name, **S**urname)
$= (\cos \theta, \sin \theta)$
$= (x, y)$

$(0, 1)$ $(\cos 90°, \sin 90°)$

$(\cos 180°, \sin 180°)$
$(-1, 0)$

S	A
T	C

$(1, 0)$
$(\cos 0°, \sin 0°)$
$(\cos 360°, \sin 360°)$

$(\cos 270°, \sin 270°)$ $(0, -1)$

(see booklet of formulae and tables, page 13)

Angles between 0° and 360°

The trigonometric ratio of an angle between 0° and 360° can be found with the following steps:

1. Make a rough diagram of the angle on a unit circle.

2. Use  to find whether this ratio is positive or negative.

3. Find its **reference** angle, the acute angle to the *x*-axis.

4. Use a calculator or the *booklet of formulae and tables* to find the ratio of the reference angle and use the sign in step 2.

Given the values of sin, cos and tan

Between 0° and 360° there may be two angles with the same trigonometric ratio, e.g. $\cos 120° = -\frac{1}{2}$ and $\cos 240° = -\frac{1}{2}$.

To find the two values, do the following:

1. Ignore the sign and evaluate the reference angle using the tables or a calculator.

2. From the sign of the given ratio, decide in which quadrants the angles can lie.

3. Using a diagram, state the angles between 0° and 360°.

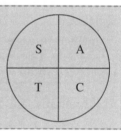

key point

It is important to know these rules for the quadrants, as your calculator will only give you the smallest of the two angles.

Example

Given that $\tan \theta = \frac{1}{\sqrt{3}}$, solve for all possible values of θ for $0 \le \theta \le 360°$.

Solution

Find the reference angle:

Reference angle $= \tan^{-1}\left(\dfrac{1}{\sqrt{3}}\right) = 30°$

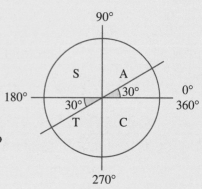

tan is positive in the 1st and 3rd quadrants.
Mark 30° from the horizontal axis into each of
these quadrants.
Read the angle from the 0° around anticlockwise to
these two marked positions.
This gives $\theta = 30°, 210°$.

Given that $\cos \theta = -\frac{1}{\sqrt{2}}$, solve for all possible values of θ for $0 \le \theta \le 360°$.

Solution

Find the reference angle by ignoring the negative sign.

Reference angle $= \cos^{-1}\left(\dfrac{1}{\sqrt{2}}\right) = 45°$.

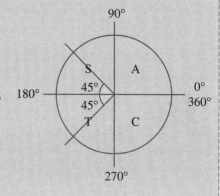

Cos is negative in the 2nd and 3rd quadrants.

Mark 45° from the horizontal axis into each of
these quadrants.

Read the angle from 0° around anticlockwise to
these two marked positions.

This gives $\theta = 135°, 225°$.

exam Q

The diagram shows a triangle ABC in which $|AB| = 6$ cm, $|CB| = 10$ cm, and $|\angle ABC| = 50°$.

(i) Calculate the area of triangle ABC, correct to the nearest cm².

(ii) Calculate the length of $[AC]$, correct to one decimal place.

(iii) The triangle $A'B'C'$ is the image of triangle ABC under the enlargement with centre B and scale factor 3. Find the area of $A'B'C'$, correct to the nearest cm².

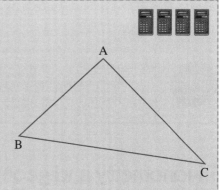

Solution

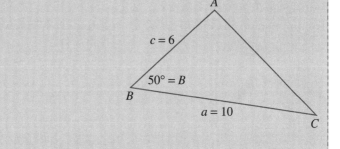

(i) Area $= \dfrac{1}{2} ac \sin B$

$= \dfrac{1}{2} (10)(6) \sin 50°$

$= (30) \sin 50°$

$= 22 \cdot 98$ cm²

$= 23$ cm²

(ii) Cosine rule:

$b^2 = a^2 + c^2 - 2ac \cos B$

$b^2 = 10^2 + 6^2 - 2(10)(6) \cos 50°$

$b^2 = 100 + 36 - 120 \cos 50°$

$b^2 = 100 + 36 - 77 \cdot 1345$

$b^2 = 58 \cdot 865$

$b = 7 \cdot 7$ cm

(iii) From enlargements:

$k^2 = \dfrac{\text{Image area}}{\text{Object area}} \Rightarrow k^2 = \dfrac{\text{Area of } A'B'C'}{\text{Area of } ABC}$

Scale factor, $k = 3$

Area of $ABC = 23$ cm²

$3^2 = \dfrac{\text{Area of } A'B'C'}{23}$

$9 = \dfrac{\text{Image area}}{23}$

$(9)(23) = \text{Image area}$

207 cm² $= \text{Area of } A'B'C'$

exam focus

Be aware of how different topics are related. Geometry and algebra methods appear regularly in trigonometry questions.

6 ▷ Trigonometry II

aims

☐ To learn to use knowledge of geometry and trigonometry in solving mathematical problems in context

Trigonometry and geometry in context

Some exam questions will require you to combine your knowledge of geometry and trigonometry to solve real-life situations. Break down the situation to a mathematical model, which you can then use to solve the problem. Refer to the **flowchart** in Trigonometry 1 to determine which rule to use when solving triangles.

exam focus

It is very important to draw a sketch of the situation. This will help you to visualise the problem and hopefully lead you to a solution.

Example

Commercial aircrafts fly at altitudes of between 9,000 m and 11,000 m. An aircraft begins its gradual descent a long distance away from its destination airport. We will assume that the path of descent is a line.

(i) An aircraft is flying at an altitude of 10,000 m and the angle of descent is 2°. At what distance, to the nearest km, from the destination runway should the descent begin?

(ii) An aircraft is flying at an altitude of 9·3 km. A passenger becomes ill and the pilot needs to land at the nearest airport, which is 200 km away. What will the angle of descent be, to two decimal places?

Solution

(i) Change 10,000 m into 10 km. Draw a diagram of the plane coming in for landing.

key point

1,000 m = 1 km

The angle on the ground is alternate to the angle of descent, so the angle on the ground is 2°.

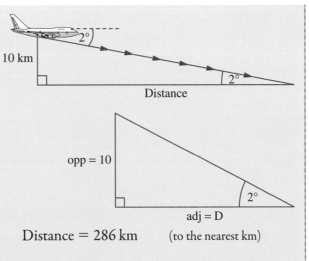

$$\tan \theta = \frac{\text{opp}}{\text{adj}}$$

$$\tan 2° = \frac{10}{\text{Distance}}$$

$$\text{Distance} = \frac{10}{\tan 2°} \quad \Rightarrow \quad \text{Distance} = 286 \text{ km} \quad \text{(to the nearest km)}$$

opp = 10

adj = D

2°

(ii) Draw a sketch of the plane coming in for landing.

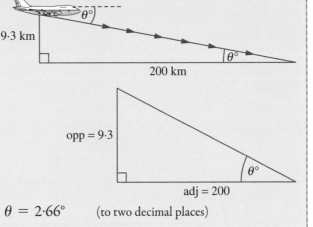

$$\tan \theta = \frac{\text{opp}}{\text{adj}}$$

$$\tan \theta = \frac{9 \cdot 3}{200}$$

$$\tan \theta = 0 \cdot 0465 \quad \Rightarrow \quad \theta = 2 \cdot 66° \quad \text{(to two decimal places)}$$

opp = 9·3

adj = 200

$\theta°$

Example

A ball at *P* is 27 m from the nearer goalpost.
 (i) Find $|\angle PRQ|$.
 (ii) Calculate the distance the ball is from the farther goalpost, to the nearest centimetre.
 (iii) Find $|\angle RPQ|$.

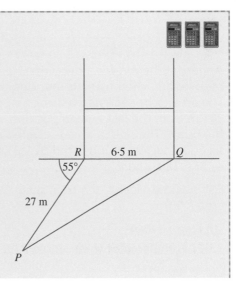

Solution

 (i) The angle at *R* is a straight angle.
$$|\angle PRQ| + 55° = 180°$$
$$|\angle PRQ| = 125°$$

(ii) Draw triangle PRQ. Use the cosine rule.
$$r^2 = p^2 + q^2 - 2pq \cos R$$
$$r^2 = (6{\cdot}5)^2 + (27)^2 - 2(6{\cdot}5)(27) \cos 125°$$
$$r^2 = 42{\cdot}25 + 729 - 2(6{\cdot}5)(27)(-0{\cdot}573576)$$
$$r^2 = 771{\cdot}25 + 201{\cdot}33$$
$$r^2 = 972{\cdot}58$$
$$r = \sqrt{972{\cdot}58}$$
$$r = 31{\cdot}186$$
Thus, $|PQ| = 3{,}118{\cdot}6$ cm.
$$|PQ| = 3{,}119 \text{ cm} \qquad \text{(correct to the nearest centimetre)}$$

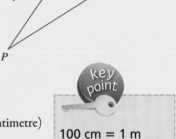

key point

100 cm = 1 m

(iii) Let $\angle RPQ$ be P. Use the sine rule and put the unknown quantity on top, or LHS.

$$\frac{\sin P}{p} = \frac{\sin R}{r}$$

$$\frac{\sin P}{6{\cdot}5} = \frac{\sin 125°}{31}$$

$$\sin P = \frac{6{\cdot}5(\sin 125°)}{31}$$

$$\sin P = 0{\cdot}17175$$

$$P = \sin^{-1}(0{\cdot}17175)$$

$$P = 9{\cdot}89°$$

Thus, $|\angle RPQ| = 9{\cdot}89°$.

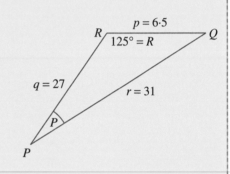

(2013 Q.8 (a))

A search is begun for a buoy that has become detached from its mooring at sea. The area to be searched is a circle of radius 30 km from the last known position, K, of the buoy. The search area is divided into six equal sectors as indicated by the letters A, B, C, D, E and F.

Fishing boats search the triangular area KAB

(i) Find $|\angle BKA|$

(ii) Find the area of the triangle KAB.

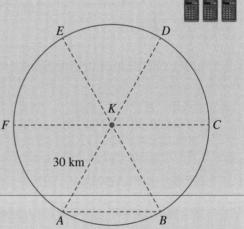

(iii) Write the area of the triangle *KAB* as a percentage of the area of the sector *KAB*.

(iv) Use the cosine rule to find the length of [*AB*].

(v) What does your answer to **(iv)** above show about the triangle *KAB*?

Solution

(i) The circle is divided into six equal sectors.

Therefore, $|\angle BKA| = \dfrac{360°}{6} = 60°$

(ii) Area of triangle $= \dfrac{1}{2}ab \sin C$

$$= \dfrac{1}{2}(30)(30) \sin 60°$$

$$= 389 \cdot 7 \text{ km}^2$$

(iii) Area of sector $= \dfrac{\theta}{360°} \times \pi r^2$

$$= \dfrac{60°}{360°} \times \pi(30)^2 = 471 \cdot 24 \text{ km}^2$$

Percentage of area $= \dfrac{\text{Area of triangle}}{\text{Area of sector}} \times 100$

$$= \dfrac{389 \cdot 7}{471 \cdot 24} \times 100 = 82 \cdot 7\%$$

(iv) $a^2 = b^2 + c^2 - 2bc \cos A$ \qquad where, $b = 30$, $c = 30$, $A = 60°$

$|AB|^2 = (30)^2 + (30)^2 - 2(30)(30) \cos 60°$

$|AB|^2 = 1800 - 900$

$|AB|^2 = 900$

$|AB| = \sqrt{900} = 30 \text{ km}$

(v) Since $|AB| = 30$ km, the three sides of the triangle *KAB* are equal. Therefore, the triangle *KAB* is equilateral.

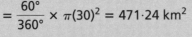

The mast of a crane [AC] is 30 m in height. By adjusting the length of the cable (from A to B), the operator of the crane can raise and lower the boom.

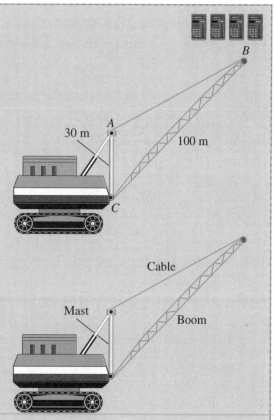

(i) What is the minimum distance possible from A to B?

(ii) When the boom of the crane, [CB], is fully lowered, point B is on the horizontal ground. At this stage the size of the angle ACB is 120°.

What is the length of the cable now between A and B, to the nearest metre?

(iii) If point C is 5 m above the ground when the boom is fully lowered to the ground, how far is the point B from the base of the crane, to two decimal places?

Solution

(i) The shortest the cable AB can be is when A and B are as close to each other as possible. This will occur when the boom is exactly vertical.

$|BC| = |AB| + |AC|$

$100 = |AB| + 30$

$70 \text{ m} = |AB|$ (minimum length)

(ii) Draw a sketch of when the crane is fully lowered and point B is on the ground. Use the cosine rule on △ABC to find |AB|, from the sketch.

$c^2 = a^2 + b^2 - 2ab \cos C$

$c^2 = 30^2 + 100^2 - 2(30)(100) \cos 120°$

$c^2 = 900 + 10{,}000 - (6{,}000)(-0{\cdot}5)$

$c^2 = 10{,}900 + 3{,}000$

$c^2 = 13{,}900$

$c = 117{\cdot}89$

Thus, $|AB| = 118$ m, correct to the nearest metre.

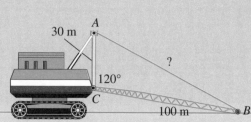

(iii) Construct the triangle with [CB] as the hypotenuse.
Use Pythagoras's theorem to find
the distance from B to the base of
the crane.

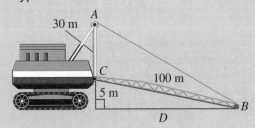

$$100^2 = 5^2 + D^2$$

$$10{,}000 = 25 + D^2$$

$$9{,}975 = D^2$$

$$99{\cdot}87 \text{ m} = D$$

exam Q

(2014 Q.9)

At an activity centre a zip-line, [BD], runs between two vertical poles, [AB] and [CD], on level ground, as shown. The point E is on the ground, directly below the zip-line.

$|AE| = 12$ m, $|BE| = 14$ m, $|CD| = 1{\cdot}95$ m, and $|EC| = 10$ m.

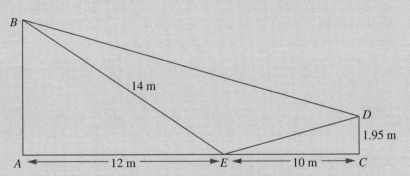

(a) **(i)** Find the distance $|ED|$, correct to one decimal place.

(ii) Find $|\angle AEB|$, correct to the nearest degree.

(b) **(i)** Find $|\angle DEB|$, given that $|\angle CED| = 11°$, correct to the nearest degree.

(ii) Hence, or otherwise, find the distance $|DB|$.

Give your answer correct to one decimal place.

Solution

(a) **(i)** Using Pythagoras's theorem:

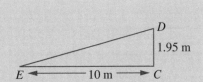

$$c^2 = a^2 + b^2$$

$$|ED|^2 = (10)^2 + (1{\cdot}95)^2$$

$$|ED|^2 = 100 + 3{\cdot}8025$$

$$|ED|^2 = 103{\cdot}8025$$

$$|ED| = \sqrt{103{\cdot}8025} = 10{\cdot}2 \text{ m}$$

(ii)
$$\cos A = \frac{\text{Adjacent}}{\text{Hypotenuse}}$$

$$\cos |\angle AEB| = \frac{12}{14}$$

$$|\angle AEB| = \cos^{-1}\left(\frac{12}{14}\right)$$

$$|\angle AEB| = 31°$$

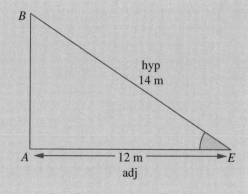

(b) (i) The three angles make a straight line:

$$31° + |\angle DEB| + 11° = 180°$$

$$|\angle DEB| + 42° = 180°$$

$$|\angle DEB| = 138°$$

(ii) $a = |BD|$, $b = 14$, $c = 10.2$, $A = 138°$

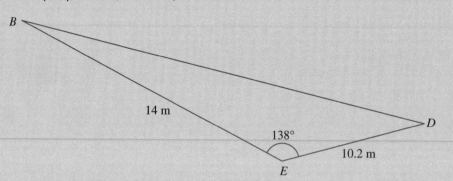

$$a^2 = b^2 + c^2 - 2bc \cos A$$

$$|BD|^2 = (14)^2 + (10.2)^2 - 2(14)(10.2) \cos 138°$$

$$|BD|^2 = 196 + 104.04 - 285.6(-0.7431448)$$

$$|BD|^2 = 300.04 + 212.242$$

$$|BD|^2 = 512.282$$

$$|BD| = \sqrt{512.282} = 22.6 \text{ m}$$

Gráinne has been out on a river in a kayak and has stopped at a point on one side of the river. However, she wants to get out on the other side. Looking across, she can only see two possible places to get out. One is a bit up the river from where she is now, and one is farther down the river. Because of the current, she can go faster towards the point down the river than the one up the river.

The situation is show in the diagram below. The banks of the river are parallel. Gráinne's position is marked G. The places where she can get out are marked A and B. The angles are as shown. The distance from B, to A is 72 metres.

If she travels in a straight line to A, Gráinne can go at 0·9 m/s and if she travels in a straight line to B, she can go at 3·2 m/s.

(i) Find the distances from G to A and from G to B.

(ii) Find the time it will take to cross by each route.

(iii) Gráinne wants to get home as fast as possible. Give one possible reason why she might **not** choose the faster of the two routes across the river.

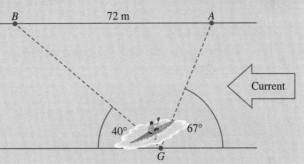

(iv) Suppose that the diagram at the start of this question is coordinated in such a way that the origin is at B, the point A lies on the positive x-axis and the units are metres.

  (a) Construct such a coordinate diagram, showing the positions of B, A and G.

  (b) Calculate the coordinates of G.

Solution

(i) $|\angle GBA| = 40°$ (alternate angles)

$|\angle GAB| = 67°$ (alternate angles)

$\therefore |\angle BGA| = 180° - 40° - 67° = 73°$

Distance from G to A:

$$\frac{|GA|}{\sin 40°} = \frac{72}{\sin 73°}$$

$$\therefore \quad |GA| = \frac{72 \sin 40°}{\sin 73°} = 48\cdot4 \text{ m}$$

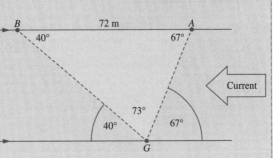

Distance from G to B:

$$= \frac{|GB|}{\sin 67°} = \frac{72}{\sin 73°}$$

$$\therefore |GB| = \frac{72 \sin 67°}{\sin 73°} = 69.3 \text{ m}$$

(ii) Time $= \dfrac{\text{Distance}}{\text{Speed}}$

Time from G to A: $t = \dfrac{48.4}{0.9} = 53.8 \text{ s}$

Time from G to B: $t = \dfrac{69.3}{3.2} = 21.65 \text{ s}$

(iii) The faster route is to go from G to B. Gráinne may not choose this route, as she may have a particular reason for wanting, or needing, to go to A. For example, point A may be the point along the river where she stores her kayak.

There is no one right answer to this 'opinion' type of question. It offers you the chance to be creative, and so long as your answer is logical and plausible, you should get the marks.

(iv) (a)

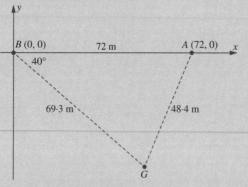

(b) To find coordinates of G, find distances x and y in the diagram.

$$\cos 40° = \frac{x}{69.3}$$

$$69.3(\cos 40°) = x$$

$$53.1 \text{ m} = x$$

$$\sin 40° = \frac{y}{69.3}$$

$$69.3(\sin 40°) = y$$

$$44.5 \text{ m} = y$$

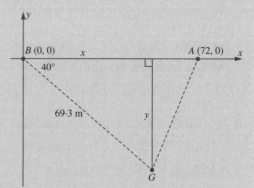

Since distance y is below the x-axis, it will be a negative coordinate.

$\therefore$ Coordinates of G = (53.1, −44.5).

Windows are sometimes in the shape of a pointed arch, like the one shown in the picture.

A person is designing such an arched window. The outline is shown in the diagram below the picture.

The centre for the arc AB is C and the centre for the arc AC is B.
|BD| = 2·4 metres and
|DE| = 1·8 metres.

(i) Show that |∠ABC| = 60°.

(ii) Find the length of the arc AB.

Give your answer in metres, correct to three decimal places.

(iii) Find the length of the perimeter of the window.

Give your answer in metres, correct to two decimal places.

(iv) Find the height of the window.

Give your answer in metres, correct to two decimal places.

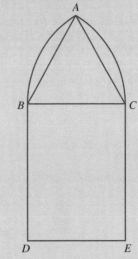

Solution

(i) Turn each arc into its full circle.

The radius of each circle is |BC| = 1·8 m. Both circles have the same radius. |AB| and |AC| are also radii in these circles.

Therefore, triangle ABC is an equilateral triangle, as its three sides are equal. The angles in an equilateral triangle are each 60°.

Therefore, |∠ABC| = 60°.

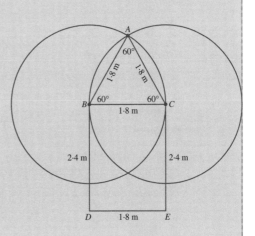

(ii) $l = \dfrac{\theta}{360°} \times 2\pi r$

$ = \dfrac{60}{360°} \times 2\pi(1\cdot8)$

$ = \dfrac{1}{6} \times 3\cdot6\pi$

$ = 0\cdot6\pi$

$ = 1\cdot885$ m

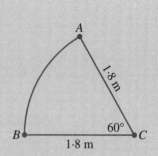

(iii) Perimeter of window $= |BD| + |DE| + |EC| + $ arc $AC + $ arc AB

$= 2\cdot4 + 1\cdot8 + 2\cdot4 + 1\cdot885 + 1\cdot885$

$= 10\cdot37$ m

(iv) To find the height of the window, we need the height of the triangle.

Use Pythagoras's theorem:
$(1\cdot8)^2 = (0\cdot9)^2 + h^2$
$3\cdot24 = 0\cdot81 + h^2$
$2\cdot43 = h^2$
$1\cdot56 = h$

Height of window $= 2\cdot4 + 1\cdot56$

$= 3\cdot96$ m

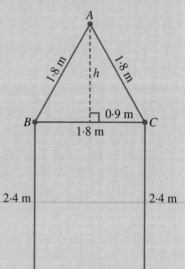

The planned supports for the roof of a building form scalene triangles of different sizes.

(i) Explain what is meant by a scalene triangle.

The triangle *EFG* is the image of the triangle *CDE* under an enlargement and the triangle *CDE* is the image of the triangle *ABC* under the same enlargement.

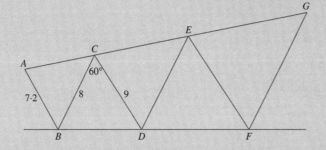

The proposed dimensions for the structure are $|AB| = 7\cdot2$ m, $|BC| = 8$ m, $|CD| = 9$ m and $|\angle DCB| = 60°$.

(ii) Find the length of [*FG*].

(iii) Find the length of [*BD*], correct to three decimal places.

(iv) The centre of the enlargement is *O*. Find the distance from *O* to the point *B*.

(v) The condition of the planning is that the height of the point *G* above the horizontal line *BD* cannot exceed 11·6 m. Does the plan meet this condition? Justify your answer by calculation.

Solution

(i) A scalene triangle is one in which the three sides have different lengths.

(ii) Find the scale factor of enlargement:

$$k = \frac{\text{Image length}}{\text{Object length}} = \frac{|CD|}{|AB|} = \frac{9}{7\cdot2} = 1\cdot25$$

Image length = k (object length)

$|ED| = 1\cdot25|CB| \Rightarrow |ED| = 1\cdot25(8) \Rightarrow |ED| = 10$ m

$|FG| = 1\cdot25|ED| \Rightarrow |FG| = 1\cdot25(10) \Rightarrow |FG| = 12\cdot5$ m

In this question, you did not need the answer to part **(i)** to continue on.

In answering a question, if you cannot answer one part of a question, don't get flustered. Move on and attempt all that you can.

(iii) Cosine rule:

$c^2 = b^2 + d^2 - 2bd \cos C$

$c^2 = 8^2 + 9^2 - 2(8)(9) \cos 60°$

$c^2 = 73$

$c = \sqrt{73} = 8{\cdot}544$ m

$\therefore |BD| = 8{\cdot}544$ m

(iv) Let the distance from O to B be x.

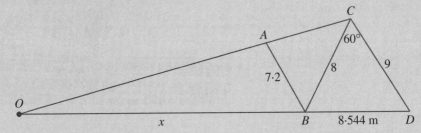

$\triangle OCD$ is an image of OAB.

$$k = \frac{\text{Image length}}{\text{Object length}} = \frac{|OD|}{|OB|}$$

$$1{\cdot}25 = \frac{x + 8{\cdot}544}{x}$$

$1{\cdot}25(x) = x + 8{\cdot}544$

$1{\cdot}25x - x = 8{\cdot}544$

$0{\cdot}25x = 8{\cdot}544$ $(\div\, 0{\cdot}25)$

$x = 34{\cdot}176$ m

(v) Use $\triangle BCD$ to find angle A.

$$\frac{\sin A}{9} = \frac{\sin 60°}{8{\cdot}544}$$

$$\sin A = \frac{9 \sin 60°}{8{\cdot}544}$$

$\sin A = 0{\cdot}9122$

In $\triangle GFJ$:

$$\sin A = \frac{h}{12{\cdot}5} \quad \Rightarrow \quad 12{\cdot}5\,(\sin A) = h \qquad \text{But } \sin A = 0{\cdot}9122$$

$12{\cdot}5(0{\cdot}9122) = h$

$11{\cdot}4$ m $= h$

Since $11{\cdot}4$ m $< 11{\cdot}6$ m, the plan meets the condition.

7 Perimeter, Area, Volume and Nets

- ☐ To clearly distinguish the difference between the units of measure, e.g. length = *m*; area = *m²*; volume = *m³*
- ☐ To know the link between various units, e.g. litres and cm³ [1 l = 1,000 cm³]
- ☐ To know where to find the relevant information in the *booklet of formulae and tables*
- ☐ To be able to recall formulae that are not in the *booklet of formulae and tables*
- ☐ To know how to calculate the perimeter and areas of regular and compound 2D shapes
- ☐ To know how to calculate the surface area and volumes of cylinders, cones, cuboids, spheres, prisms and compound shapes
- ☐ To understand and be able to draw nets
- ☐ To gain the exam savvy to apply the above knowledge in real-life exam-type questions

Perimeter and area

Example

The diagram shows a rectangle of length 42 cm. The area of the rectangle is 966 cm².

(i) Find the height of the rectangle.
(ii) Find the area of the shaded triangle.

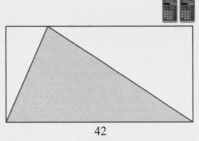

42

Solution

(i) Equation given in disguise:

Note: the height of the rectangle is the same as the breadth

Area rectangle = length × breadth

$$966 = l \times b$$
$$966 = 42 \times b$$
$$23 \text{ cm} = b$$

(ii) Area of shaded triangle

$$\text{Area} \triangle = \tfrac{1}{2}(\text{base})(\text{perpendicular ht})$$

(see *booklet of formulae and tables*, page 9)

$$\text{Area} = \tfrac{1}{2}(42)(23)$$
$$= \tfrac{1}{2}(966)$$
$$= 483 \text{ cm}^2$$

exam focus

You must know the formula for the area of a rectangle, as it is **not** in the *booklet of formulae and tables*.

Example

A patio tile in the shape of a trapezium, with dimensions as shown, is given in the diagram. Find the area of the tile.

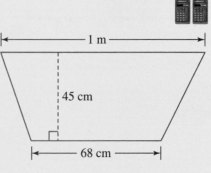

Solution

$$\text{Area of trapezium} = \left(\frac{a + b}{2}\right)h$$

(see *booklet of formulae and tables*, page 8)

$h = 45\text{ cm};\quad a = 68\text{ cm};\quad b = 1\text{ m} = 100\text{ cm}$ (all dimensions in cm)

$$\therefore \text{ Area of the tile} = \left(\frac{68 + 100}{2}\right)(45) = 3{,}780\text{ cm}^2 = 0{\cdot}378\text{ m}^2$$

key point

The question did not specify whether to give the answer in cm^2 or m^2. In this case, either will be acceptable. Remember, 1 m^2 = 100 × 100 cm^2.

(2017 Q.4 (b))

The diagram shows a square of side length 2k cm.

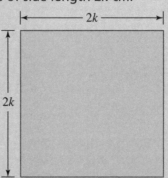

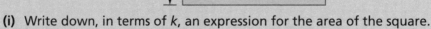

(i) Write down, in terms of k, an expression for the area of the square.

(ii) An isosceles triangle with side lengths of 20 cm and hypotenuse of length $2k$ cm is removed from the square, as shown.

Find the value of k (correct to two decimal places) **and** the area of the remaining (shaded) section.

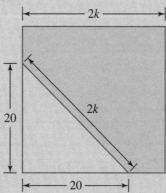

Solution

(i) Area of square $= (2k)(2k) = 4k^2 \text{ cm}^2$

(ii)

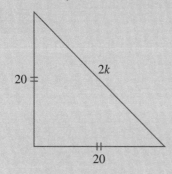

Area of non-shaded triangle $= \dfrac{1}{2}(20)(20) = 200$

Pythagoras's theorem: $(2k)^2 = (20)^2 + (20)^2$

$$4k^2 = 400 + 400 = 800$$
$$k^2 = 200$$
$$k = 14.14 \text{ cm}$$

Area of shaded section = area of square − area of non-shaded triangle

$$= 4k^2 - 200$$
$$= 800 - 200$$
$$= 600 \text{ cm}^2 \text{ (or } 599.7584 \text{ cm}^2)$$

key point

- π is a ratio of the circumference of any circle to its diameter.
- $\pi = 3\cdot141592 \ldots$ is known nowadays to billions of decimal places.
- In the exam we may be told to take π as a particular value, e.g $\frac{22}{7}$, $3\cdot14$.
- When using $\pi = \frac{22}{7}$, it is good practice to write the radius as a fraction, e.g. $3\cdot5 = \frac{7}{2}$ or $18 = \frac{18}{1}$.
- If a question says 'give your answer in terms of π', then leave π in the answer. Do not use $3\cdot14$ or $\frac{22}{7}$ for π.
- If you are not given an approximate value for π, then you must use the value given by the calculator.

Example

The area of a circle is 81π cm^2. Its length is $k\pi$ cm. Calculate k.

Solution

Equation given in disguise:	Length (circumference) of a circle
Area $= 81\pi$ cm^2	$= 2\pi r$
$\therefore \pi r^2 = 81\pi$	$= 2\pi(9)$ (put in $r = 9$)
$r^2 = 81$	$= 18\pi$ cm
$r = 9$ cm	Comparing: $k\pi = 18\pi$
	$\therefore k = 18$

Sally makes earrings from silver wire.

Her design includes two touching sectors of circles, as shown in the diagram.

The inner arc has centre Q, radius 1·4 cm.

The outer arc has centre B, radius 3 cm.

$|\angle ABC| = 60°$ and $|\angle PQR| = 108°$

(i) Find the total length of silver wire required by Sally to make this earring. Give your answer correct to the nearest millimetre.

(ii) Allowing 10% for waste when making each earring, how many earrings will Sally make from a 1 m length of silver wire?

(iii) Hence, comment on how Sally could improve her manufacturing process.

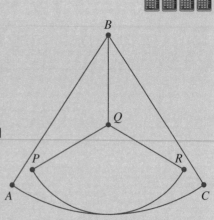

Solution

(i) $|AB| = |CB| = 3$ and $|PQ| = |RQ| = 1·4$ and $|BQ| = 3 - 1·4 = 1·6$

Length of arc $PR = \dfrac{108°}{360°}(2\pi r) = 0·3(2\pi(1·4)) = 2·638937829$

Length of arc $AC = \dfrac{60°}{360°}(2\pi r) = \dfrac{1}{6}(2\pi(3)) = 3·141592654$

Total length of silver wire in earring

$= |AB| + |CB| + |PQ| + |RQ| + |BQ| + $ arc $PR + $ arc AC

$= 3 + 3 + 1·4 + 1·4 + 1·6 + 2·6389 + 3·1415$

$= 16·1804$ cm

$= 162$ mm

(ii) 162 mm + 10% waste = 162 + 16·2 = 178·2 mm

1 m = 1,000 mm

∴ Sally can make $\frac{1,000}{178·2}$ = 5·61167 . . .
five earrings from 1 m of silver wire.

(iii) If Sally could eliminate the 10% waste,
she could make $\frac{1,000}{162}$ = 6·17 . . .
six earrings from 1 m of silver wire.

The examiners consistently ask
questions that require candidates
to apply the mathematics they
learn to real-life (in-context)
situations.

Volume of rectangular objects

1. Rectangular solid (cuboid)

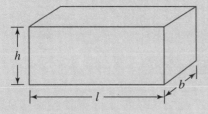

Volume = lbh
Surface area = $2lb + 2lh + 2bh$

2. Cube

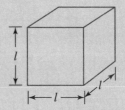

Volume = l^3
Surface area = $6l^2$

The above formulae are **not** in the *booklet of formulae and tables*.
You must know them.

Example

The volume of a rectangular block is 560 cm³.
If its length is 14 cm and its breadth is 8 cm, find
(i) its height and (ii) its surface area.

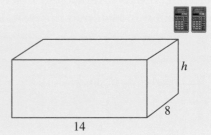

Solution

(i) Equation given in disguise:

Volume = 560 cm³

$(14)(8)h = 560$

$112h = 560$

$h = \dfrac{560}{112} = 5$ cm

(ii) Surface area = $2lb + 2lh + 2bh$

$= 2(14)(8) + 2(14)(5) + 2(8)(5)$

$= 224 + 140 + 80$

$= 444$ cm²

Uniform cross-sections and nets

Many solid objects have the same cross-section throughout their length. Here are some examples.

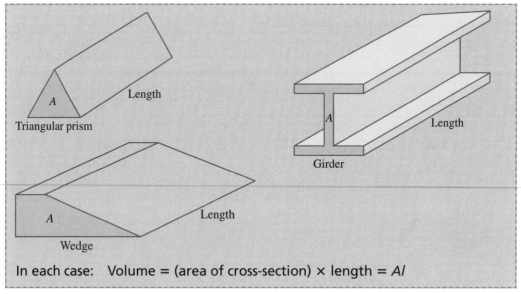

Triangular prism

Girder

Wedge

Length

In each case: Volume = (area of cross-section) × length = Al

The above objects are called prisms. A prism is a solid object which has the same cross-section throughout its length and its sides are parallelograms.

A solid cylinder has a uniform cross-section, but it is not a prism.

So to find the volume of a solid object with a uniform cross-section, find the area of the cross-section and multiply this by its length.

Example

This triangular prism has a volume of 513 cm². Work out the length of the base of its cross-section.

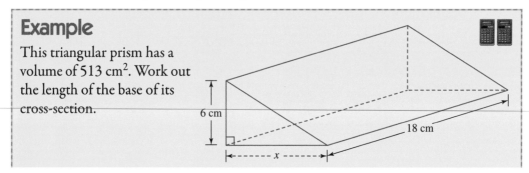

6 cm

18 cm

x

Solution

The volume of prism = (area of cross section) × length

An equation given in disguise:

$$\text{Volume} = 513$$

$$(\text{Area of triangle})\, l = 513$$

$$\frac{1}{2}(x)(6)(18) = 513$$

$$54x = 513 \qquad \text{(divide both sides by 54)}$$

$$x = 9\cdot5 \text{ cm}$$

Example

This prism is 8 cm long.
The ends are equilateral triangles with sides
of 4 cm.
Draw an accurate net of the prism.

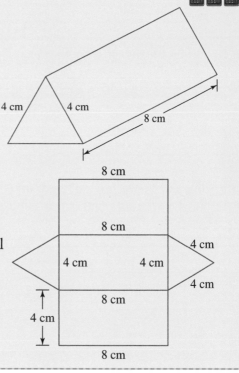

4 cm   4 cm   8 cm

Solution

Step 1: Draw the rectangular faces of the
prism. Each rectangle is 8 cm long
and 4 cm wide.

Step 2: The ends of the prism are equilateral
triangles.
The length of each side of the
triangles is 4 cm.
Use your compass to construct the
equilateral triangles.

8 cm

8 cm

4 cm   4 cm   4 cm

4 cm

8 cm   4 cm

8 cm

exam
Q

The diagram shows a winners' podium with a square base of 90 cm.
The heights of 2nd place : 1st place : 3rd place
sections of the podium are in the ratio
5 : 7 : 3 respectively.

Given that the total volume of the podium is
324 litres, find the height of each section.

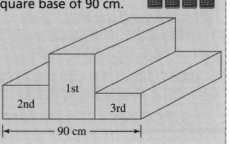

1st

2nd   3rd

90 cm

Solution

Let the heights of each section be 5h, 7h
and 3h respectively.

Cross section area = (5h)(30) + (7h)(30) + (3h)(30)

$$= 150h + 210h + 90h$$

$$= 450h$$

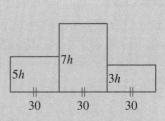

Volume of podium = 324 litres = 324 × 1,000 = 324,000 cm³

Equation given in disguise:

Volume of podium = (area of cross-section) × length

$$324,000 = (450h)(90)$$

$$324,000 = 40,500h$$

$$8 = h$$

Heights are 5h : 7h : 3h
= 40 cm : 56 cm : 24 cm respectively.

key point

- We need 1l = 1,000 cm³
- Volume of podium = (area of cross section) × length

exam Q

(i) Which of the following, diagram P or diagram Q, is the
net of a cylinder? Justify your choice.

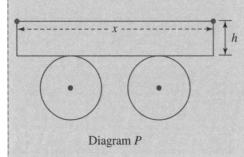

Diagram P

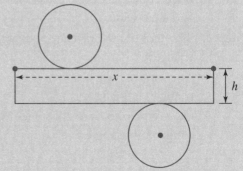

Diagram Q

(ii) Given that the identical circles have a diameter of 20 m, write down the
radius of the circles.

(iii) If the volume of the cylinder is 2,512 m², using volume = $\pi r^2 h$, solve for h.
Assume π = 3·14.

(iv) Calculate x, the length of the rectangle.

(v) The cylinder is used as a military bunker. For security reasons the entire
cylinder is to be covered by a copper mesh at a cost of €295 per square
metre. Find the cost of the copper required to the nearest €1,000.

Solution

(i) Diagram Q is the net of a cylinder.

Diagram P is not the net of a cylinder because both circles are on the bottom.

(ii) Diameter $= 2r = 20$ $\therefore$ $r = 10$ m

(iii)
$$\pi r^2 h = 2{,}512$$
$$3 \cdot 14(10)^2 h = 2{,}512$$
$$314h = 2{,}512$$
$$h = 8 \text{ m}$$

(iv) Since Q is the net of a cylinder, then x, the length of the rectangle, equals the circumference of the circle.

$\therefore$ $x = 2\pi r$

$x = 2(3 \cdot 14)(10)$

$x = 62 \cdot 8$ m

(v) Total surface area of cylinder $= \bigcirc + \bigcirc + \boxed{}$

$= \pi r^2 + \pi r^2 + xh$

$= (3 \cdot 14)(10)^2 + (3 \cdot 14)(10)^2 + (62 \cdot 8)(8)$

$= 314 + 314 + 502 \cdot 4$

$= 1{,}130 \cdot 4$ m^2

The total cost $= 1{,}130 \cdot 4 \times 295 = 333{,}468$

$= €333{,}000$ (to the nearest thousand)

exam focus

Using the net of the cylinder makes the solution to **(v)** above very simple.

Compound volumes

You may be asked to find the volume of an object which is made up of different shapes.

When this happens, do the following:

1. Split the solid up into regular shapes, for which we have formulae to calculate the volume or surface area.
2. Add these results together.

exam Q

(2015 Q.8)

(a) A company has a spherical storage tank. The diameter of the tank is 12 m.

　(i) Write down the radius of the tank.

　(ii) Find the volume of the tank, correct to the nearest m³.

(b) The company paints the outside curved surface of the spherical tank.

　(i) Find the curved surface area of the tank, correct to one decimal place.

　(ii) The curved surface is painted with a special paint. One litre of paint will cover 3·5 m². Find how many litres of paint are used, correct to the nearest litre.

　(iii) The paint is sold in 25-litre tins. Each tin costs €180. Find the total cost of the paint.

(c) At another site, the company has a differently-shaped tank with the same volume. This tank has hemispherical ends and a cylindrical mid-section of length h m, as shown.

The radius of each hemispherical end is 4·5 m.

　(i) Find the volume of one hemispherical end, correct to the nearest m³.

　(ii) Find the length, h, of the cylindrical section, correct to one decimal place.

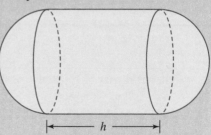

Solution

(a) (i) Radius $= \dfrac{1}{2}(12) = 6$ m

　(ii) Volume of sphere $= \dfrac{4}{3}\pi r^3 = \dfrac{4}{3}\pi(6)^3 = 905$ cm³

(b) (i) Curved surface of sphere $= 4\pi r^2 = 4\pi(6)^2 = 452\cdot4$ m²

　(ii) Number of litres required $= \dfrac{452\cdot4}{3\cdot5} = 129\cdot26 = 130\,l$

　(iii) Number of tins required $= \dfrac{130}{25} = 5\cdot2$ tins

　　To buy 6 tins (cannot buy 5·2 tins) costs $6 \times 180 = €1{,}080$

(c) (i) Volume of $\dfrac{1}{2}$ sphere $= \dfrac{1}{2} \times \dfrac{4}{3}\pi r^3 = \dfrac{2}{3}\pi(4\cdot5)^3 = 191$ m³

　(ii) This tank has same volume as in part **(a)(ii)** = 905 m³

　　This means hemisphere + cylinder + hemisphere = 905

$$191 + \pi r^2 h + 191 = 905$$

$$\pi(4\cdot5)^2 h = 523$$

$$h = 8\cdot2 \text{ m}$$

Four identical spheres fit exactly into a cuboid, the plan of which is shown in the diagram. Given that $|AC| = 6\sqrt{2}$ cm, find:

(i) The radius of a sphere
(ii) The volume of the space in the cuboid not occupied by the spheres, correct to the nearest integer.

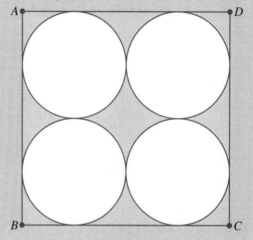

Solution

(i)

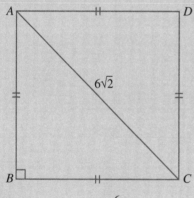

Let x = length of each side of square

From Pythagoras, we write:

$$|AC|^2 = |AB|^2 + |BC|^2$$
$$(6\sqrt{2})^2 = x^2 + x^2$$
$$72 = 2x^2$$
$$36 = x^2 \quad \Rightarrow \quad 6 \text{ cm} = x$$

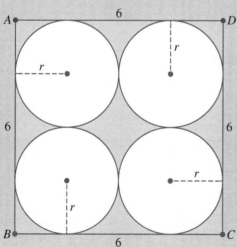

From diagram, $4r = 6$.

$$\therefore \text{ Radius} = r = \frac{6}{4} = \frac{3}{2} \text{ cm}$$

(ii) Volume of cuboid $= l \times b \times h$

$= 6 \times 6 \times 2r$

$= 6 \times 6 \times 2\left(\dfrac{3}{2}\right)$

$= 108 \text{ cm}^3$

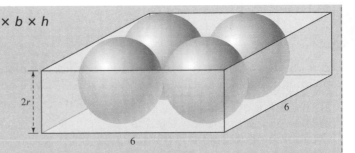

Volume of 4 spheres $= 4\left(\dfrac{4}{3}\pi r^3\right)$

$= \dfrac{16}{3}\pi\left(\dfrac{3}{2}\right)^3 = \dfrac{16}{3}\pi\left(\dfrac{27}{8}\right) = 18\pi \text{ cm}^3$

Volume of cuboid not occupied by spheres $= 108 - 18\pi = 51 \text{ cm}^3$

A right circular cone *M* has dimensions given in cm, as in the diagram. *M* is divided horizontally to its base into two sections, *J* and *K*, as shown in the diagram.

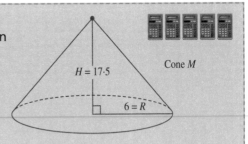

Cone *M*

$H = 17.5$

$6 = R$

(i) Write down the radius, *r*, of the cone *J*. Justify your answer for *r*.

(ii) Find the volume of *J*. Assume $\pi = \dfrac{22}{7}$.

Cone *J*

$h = 7$

r

(iii) Find the volume of the (frustum) section *K*. Assume $\pi = \dfrac{22}{7}$.

Solution

(i) Given the dimensions, *R, H, r, h* as in the diagram, and the fact that the base of the small cone is parallel to the large cone.

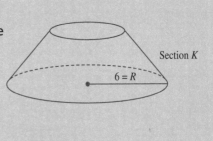

Section *K*

$6 = R$

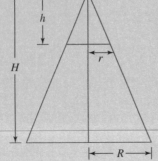

key point

M divided horizontally means that the base of the cones are parallel.

We have the following result:

$$\frac{h}{H} = \frac{r}{R}$$

or in words $\dfrac{\text{Smaller height}}{\text{Larger height}} = \dfrac{\text{Smaller radius}}{\text{Larger radius}}$

In this case, $H = 17\cdot5$, $h = 7$, $R = 6$, then we can solve for r.

$$\Rightarrow \quad \frac{7}{17\cdot5} = \frac{r}{6}$$

$$\frac{7 \times 6}{17\cdot5} = r$$

$$2\cdot4 \text{ cm} = r$$

This is an application of a geometry theorem that states: 'If two triangles are similar, then the lengths of their corresponding sides are proportional.'

(ii) Volume of $J = \dfrac{1}{3}\pi r^2 h = \dfrac{1}{3}\left(\dfrac{22}{7}\right)(2\cdot4)^2(7) = 42\cdot24 \text{ cm}^3$

(iii) Volume of section K = volume of cone M − volume of cone J

$$= \frac{1}{3}\pi R^2 H - 42\cdot24$$

$$= \frac{1}{3}\left(\frac{22}{7}\right)(6)^2(17\cdot5) - 42\cdot24$$

$$= 660 - 42\cdot24$$

$$= 617\cdot76 \text{ cm}^3$$

Alternatively for **(iii)** you may use the formula for a frustum from the *booklet of formulae and tables*, page 11.

Displaced liquid

In many questions we have to deal with situations where liquid is displaced by immersing, or removing, a solid object. In all cases, the following principle helps us to solve these problems:

Volume of displaced liquid = Volume of immersed solid object

(i) Find the volume of a solid sphere with a diameter of length 3 cm. Give your answer in terms of π.

(ii) A cylindrical vessel with internal diameter of length 15 cm contains water. The surface of the water is 11 cm from the top of the vessel.

How many solid spheres, each with diameter of length 3 cm, must be placed in the vessel in order to bring the surface of the water to 1 cm from the top of the vessel? Assume that all the spheres are submerged in the water.

Solution

(i) Diameter = 3, which means radius = $\dfrac{3}{2}$.

Volume of sphere = $\dfrac{4}{3}\pi r^3 = \dfrac{4}{3}\pi\left(\dfrac{3}{2}\right)^3 = \dfrac{4}{3}\pi\left(\dfrac{27}{8}\right) = \pi\left(\dfrac{9}{2}\right)$ cm^3

(ii) Diameter = 15, which means radius = $\dfrac{15}{2}$.

Note: The height of the red cylinder = 11 − 1 = 10 cm.

Volume of the red cylinder = $\pi r^2 h$

$= \pi\left(\dfrac{15}{2}\right)^2(10) = \pi\left(\dfrac{225}{4}\right)(10) = \pi\,\dfrac{1{,}125}{2}$ cm^3

How many spheres are required to fill this red cylinder?

The number of spheres required $= \dfrac{\text{Volume of red cylinder}}{\text{Volume of one sphere}}$

$= \dfrac{\pi\,\frac{1{,}125}{2}}{\pi\,\frac{9}{2}} = \left(\dfrac{1{,}125}{2}\right)\left(\dfrac{2}{9}\right) = 125$ spheres

Recasting

Many of the questions we meet require us to solve a recasting problem. What happens is that a certain solid object is melted down and its shape is changed. We use the following fact:

> The volume remains the same after it is melted down unless we are told otherwise in the question.

A solid is in the shape of a hemisphere surmounted by a cone, as in the diagram opposite.

The total volume of the solid is $\dfrac{507}{4}\pi$ cm^3.

This solid is melted down and recast in the shape of a solid cylinder. The height of the cylinder is 12 cm.

Calculate the radius of this cylinder.

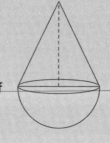

Solution

Volume cone + Volume hemisphere = Volume cylinder.

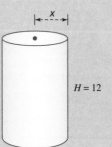

$$\frac{507}{4}\pi = \pi x^2 H$$

$$\frac{507}{4} = x^2(12)$$

$$10\cdot5625 = x^2$$

$$3\cdot25 \text{ cm} = x$$

Moving liquids

In many questions we have to deal with moving liquid from one container to another container of different dimensions or shape. Again, to help us solve the problem we use the fact that:

The volume of the moved liquid does not change unless we are told otherwise in the question.

(i) In Turlough Hill, a pumped storage hydro-electric power station, water issues from a cylindrical pipe of internal diameter 2·4 m at a rate of 29 m³ per second. At what speed is the water flowing through the pipe? Give your answer in m/sec, correct to one decimal place.

(ii) Hence or otherwise, if the diameter of the pipe was 1·2 m, find, correct to one decimal place, the new speed of the water in m/sec given that the rate of flow remained 29 m³ per second.

(iii)

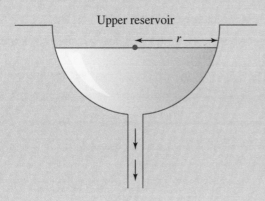

Upper reservoir

The cylindrical pipe drains water from an upper reservoir, which is in the shape of a hemisphere. It takes 4 hours at a constant flow rate of 29 m³ per second to empty the upper reservoir. Find, correct to the nearest integer, the depth in metres of the water in the upper reservoir before the water began to flow.

Solution

(i)

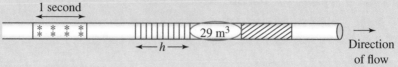

- Diameter 2·4 m $\Rightarrow$ Radius = 1·2 m
- Flow in pipe can be considered at 1-second intervals.

1 second

29 m³

$\leftarrow h \rightarrow$

Direction of flow

Then speed is h m/sec.
Rate of flow is 29 m³/sec.

An equation given in disguise:

Volume of water per second = volume of cylinder = $\pi r^2 h$

$$29 = \pi(1·2)^2 h$$

$$6·4104 = h$$

$$\text{Speed} = 6·4 \text{ m/sec}$$

(ii) If diameter halved (2·4 m $\rightarrow$ 1·2 m), then radius = 0·6 m.

Flow rate unchanged means $29 = \pi(0·6)^2 h$.

$$25·6 = h \Rightarrow \text{Speed } 25·6 \text{ m/sec}$$

The radius in part **(ii)** is half radius in part **(i)**.

Radius halved means r^2 decreases by a factor of $\left(\frac{1}{2}\right)^2 = \frac{1}{4}$.

Hence, to compensate for this decrease $\left(\text{of } \frac{1}{4}\right)$, the speed must increase by a factor of 4 if the rate of flow is unchanged.

This explains why $6·4 \times 4 = 25·6$ gives a very quick solution to this question.

(iii)

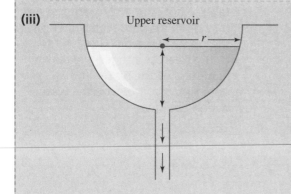

Upper reservoir

$\leftarrow r \rightarrow$

Flow rate of 29 m³/sec means

$29 \times 60 \times 60 \times 4 = 417{,}600$ m³ in 4 hours.

Vol. hemisphere reservoir = $\frac{2}{3}\pi r^3$

$$417{,}600 = \frac{2}{3}\pi r^3$$

$$58·420 = r$$

Depth = 58 m to nearest integer

(2017 Q.7)

Cones is a sculpture in the National Gallery of Australia. It consists of 14 identical steel cones arranged into pairs, which are joined together as shown.

© russellstreet

(a) (i) The height of each cone is equal to the diameter of its base. If the radius of the base is 2·25 m, write the height of a cone.

(ii) Show that, correct to two decimal places, the slant height, l, of a cone is 5·03 m.

(b) In order to maintain the steel's reflective shine, the surface is polished regularly.

(i) Find the curved surface area of the entire sculpture (14 cones). Give your answer correct to two decimal places.

(ii) One litre of polish will cover 12·25 m². Find how many litres are needed to polish the entire sculpture. Give your answer correct to the nearest litre.

(iii) A container of polish contains 5 litres and costs A\$110. Find the number of containers of polish that must be purchased in order to polish the entire sculpture and hence find the cost of the polish in Euro (A\$1 = €0·68). Give your answer correct to the nearest Euro.

(c) The diagram (not to scale) shows the net of the outer surface of one of the cones of the sculpture. It is a sector of a circle of radius length 5·03 m with arc length p m and angle θ at the centre, as shown below.

(i) Find p, the length of the arc of the sector. Give your answer correct to two decimal places.

(ii) Find θ, the angle at the centre of the sector. Show all your working out. Give your answer to the nearest degree.

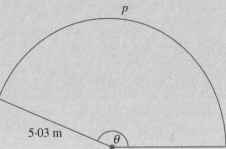

Solution

(a) (i) h = diameter = 2(radius) = 2(2·25) = 4·5 m

(ii)

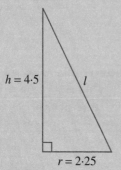

Using Pythagoras's theorem:
$$l^2 = h^2 + r^2$$
$$l^2 = (4·5)^2 + (2·25)^2$$
$$l^2 = 25·3125$$
$$l = 5·03 \text{ m as required}$$

(b) (i) Curved surface of cone = $\pi r l$ = $\pi(2·25)(5·03)$ = 35·5549 m^2

Curved surface of 14 such cones = 14 × 35·5549 = 497·77 m^2

(ii) Number of litres of polish required = $\dfrac{497·77}{12·25}$ = 40·6 = 41 litres

(iii) Number of containers required = $\dfrac{41}{5}$ = 8·2 = 9 containers

Cost in A\$ = 9 × 110 = A\$990

Cost in € = 990 × 0 · 68 = €673 or €674

(c) (i) Length of arc p = circumference of the base of one of the cones

$p = 2\pi r$

$p = 2\pi(2·25)$

$p = 14·137$

$p = 14·14$ m

(ii) Arc of sector = $\left(\dfrac{\theta}{360}\right) \times 2\pi(r)$

$14·14 = \left(\dfrac{\theta}{360}\right) \times 2\pi(5·03)$

$\dfrac{(14·14)(360)}{2\pi(5·03)} = \theta$

$161° = \theta$

8 The Trapezoidal Rule and Its Applications

aims

☐ To know where to find the general form of the formula for the trapezoidal rule in the *booklet of formulae and tables*

☐ To develop the skill of applying the trapezoidal rule for specific cases, e.g. when the number of strips is 5 or when we are given an equation in disguise

☐ To know we can be asked to take measurements from a drawing (either in cm or using a scale) and apply the trapezoidal rule with the numbers we have found

☐ To acquire the skill necessary to apply the trapezoidal rule to in-context and procedural exam questions

Trapezoidal rule

The trapezoidal rule gives a concise formula to enable us to make a good approximation of the area of an irregular shape. Consider the diagram below.

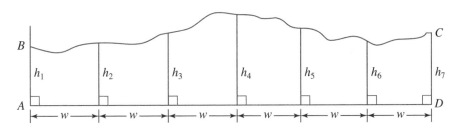

To find the area of the figure *ABCD*, do the following:

1. Divide the figure into a number of strips of equal width. (Note: The number of strips can be even or odd.)
2. Number and measure each height, h.
3. Use the following formula:

$$\text{Area} = \frac{w}{2}[h_1 + h_7 + 2(h_2 + h_3 + h_4 + h_5 + h_6)]$$

$$\text{Area} = \frac{\text{Width}}{2}[\text{first height} + \text{last height} + 2(\text{sum of all remaining heights})]$$

key point

- The greater the number of strips taken, the greater the accuracy.
- The trapezoidal rule lends itself very well to real-life situations, e.g. area of a lake or building site.
- See the *booklet of formulae and tables* page 12 for the general formula for the trapezoidal rule.
- As in the following exam questions the base of the shape does not have to be straight.

exam Q

Archaeologists excavating a rectangular plot *ABCD* measuring 60 m by 50 m divided the plot into 10 equal rectangular sections, as shown on the diagram. At the end of the first phase of the work, the shaded area had been excavated. To estimate the area excavated, perpendicular measurements were made to the edge of the excavated area, as shown.

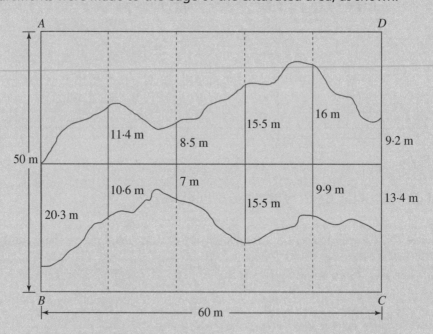

(i) Use the trapezoidal rule to estimate the area excavated in m².

(ii) Express the excavated area as a percentage of the rectangular plot, correct to the nearest integer.

Solution

(i) The length of the rectangular area is 60 m. It is divided up into five equal strips.

$$\therefore \text{ The width of one strip } = \frac{60}{5} = 12 \text{ m.}$$

$$\text{Area} = \frac{\text{Width}}{2}[h_1 + h_6 + 2(h_2 + h_3 + h_4 + h_5)]$$

Width = 12 m

$h_1 = 0 + 20\cdot3 = 20\cdot3$ m $h_4 = 15\cdot5 + 15\cdot5 = 31$ m

$h_2 = 11\cdot4 + 10\cdot6 = 22$ m $h_5 = 16 + 9\cdot9 = 25\cdot9$ m

$h_3 = 8\cdot5 + 7 = 15\cdot5$ m $h_6 = 9\cdot2 + 13\cdot4 = 22\cdot6$ m

key point

> This example shows how we merge two irregular shapes together (by adding the respective heights) and apply one application of the trapezoidal rule instead of two applications.

$$\text{Area} = \frac{12}{2}[20\cdot3 + 22\cdot6 + 2(22 + 15\cdot5 + 31 + 25\cdot9)]$$

$$= 6[42\cdot9 + 2(94\cdot4)]$$

$$= 6[42\cdot9 + 188\cdot8]$$

$$= 1,390\cdot2 \text{ m}^2$$

(ii) Area of rectangular plot = $60 \times 50 = 3,000$ m^2

Excavated area as a percentage of the rectangular plot

$$= \frac{\text{Area of excavated region}}{\text{Area of rectangular plot}} \times 100\%$$

$$= \frac{1,390\cdot2}{3,000} \times 100\% = 46\%$$

(2017 Paper 1 Q.5)

(a) A field is divided into eight sections as shown below. The width of each section is 3 metres. The height, in metres, of each section is given in the diagram.

Use the trapezoidal rule to estimate the area of the field.

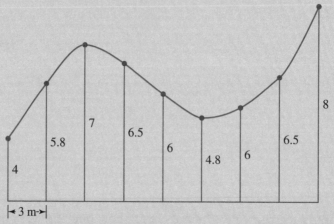

(b) The area of the same field was re-estimated by applying the trapezoidal rule again.

This time, a different section width (4 m) and a different set of section heights were used, as shown below.

The area was found to be 145·6 m².

Use this information to find the value of the height marked x on the diagram.

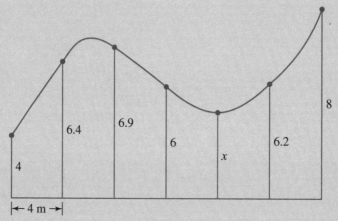

The above question was asked in the 2017 exam on Paper 1. Previously, such questions appeared exclusively on Paper 2.

This is the examiner warning us to expect the unexpected!

Solution

(a) Given values

$w = 3$	$h_3 = 7$	$h_6 = 4 \cdot 8$	$h_9 = 8$
$h_1 = 4$	$h_4 = 6 \cdot 5$	$h_7 = 6$	
$h_2 = 5 \cdot 8$	$h_5 = 6$	$h_8 = 6 \cdot 5$	

$$\text{Area} = \frac{w}{2}[h_1 + h_9 + 2(h_2 + h_3 + h_4 + h_5 + h_6 + h_7 + h_8)]$$

$$= \frac{3}{2}[4 + 8 + 2(5 \cdot 8 + 7 + 6 \cdot 5 + 6 + 4 \cdot 8 + 6 + 6 \cdot 5)]$$

$$= \frac{3}{2}[4 + 8 + 2(42 \cdot 6)] = 145 \cdot 8 \text{ m}^2$$

(b) In this part, the equation is given in disguise:

Given values:

$w = 4$	$h_3 = 6 \cdot 9$	$h_6 = 6 \cdot 2$
$h_1 = 4$	$h_4 = 6$	$h_7 = 8$
$h_2 = 6 \cdot 4$	$h_5 = x$	

$$145 \cdot 6 = \frac{w}{2}[h_1 + h_7 + 2(h_2 + h_3 + h_4 + h_5 + h_6)]$$

$$145 \cdot 6 = \frac{4}{2}[4 + 8 + 2(6 \cdot 4 + 6 \cdot 9 + 6 + x + 6 \cdot 2)]$$

$$145 \cdot 6 = \frac{4}{2}[4 + 8 + 2(25 \cdot 5 + x)]$$

$$145 \cdot 6 = 2[12 + 51 + 2x]$$

$$145 \cdot 6 = 24 + 102 + 4x$$

$$145 \cdot 6 - 24 - 102 = 4x$$

$$19 \cdot 6 = 4x$$

$$4 \cdot 9 = x$$

The diagram shows the curve $y = x^2$ in the domain $1 \le x \le 4$ when $x \in \mathbb{R}$.

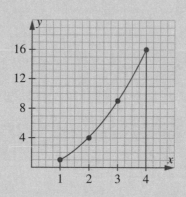

(i) Copy the following table, then complete it using the equation of the curve.

x	1	1·5	2	2·5	3	3·5	4
y							

(ii) Hence, use the trapezoidal rule to estimate the area between the curve and the x-axis when

    (a) Width $w = 1$ **(b)** Width $w = \dfrac{1}{2}$.

(iii) Given that the exact answer is 21 units², find the percentage error in the area for

    (a) $w = 1$ **(b)** $w = \dfrac{1}{2}$.

    Give both answers correct to one decimal place.

(iv) State which answer, **(a)** or **(b)**, gives the most accurate result. Justify your statement.

Solution

(i) Note: $(1)^2 = 1$; $(1\cdot5)^2 = 2\cdot25$; $(2)^2 = 4$; $(2\cdot5)^2 = 6\cdot25$; $(3)^2 = 9$; $(3\cdot5)^2 = 12\cdot25$; $(4)^2 = 16$. This gives:

x	1	1·5	2	2·5	3	3·5	4
$y = x^2$	1	2·25	4	6·25	9	12·25	16

(ii) Using the trapezoidal rule twice:

(a) $w = 1$

$h_1 = 1$
$h_2 = 4$
$h_3 = 9$
$h_4 = 16$

$$\text{Area} = \frac{w}{2}[h_1 + h_4 + 2(h_2 + h_3)]$$

$$= \frac{1}{2}[1 + 16 + 2(4 + 9)]$$

$$= \frac{1}{2}[17 + 26]$$

$$= \frac{1}{2}[43]$$

$$= 21 \cdot 5 \text{ units}^2$$

(b) $w = \frac{1}{2}$ $h_4 = 6 \cdot 25$

$h_1 = 1$ $h_5 = 9$
$h_2 = 2 \cdot 25$ $h_6 = 12 \cdot 25$
$h_3 = 4$ $h_7 = 16$

$$\text{Area} = \frac{w}{2}[h_1 + h_7 + 2(h_2 + h_3 + h_4 + h_5 + h_6)]$$

$$= \frac{\frac{1}{2}}{2}[1 + 16 + 2(2 \cdot 25 + 4 + 6 \cdot 25 + 9 + 12 \cdot 25)]$$

$$= \frac{1}{4}[17 + 2(33 \cdot 75)]$$

$$= \frac{1}{4}[17 + 67 \cdot 5]$$

$$= \frac{1}{4}[84 \cdot 5]$$

$$= 21 \cdot 125 \text{ units}^2$$

(iii)

key point

$$\text{The percentage error} = \frac{|\text{True value} - \text{estimate}|}{\text{True value}} \times 100\%$$

(a) The percentage error

$$= \frac{|21 - 21 \cdot 5|}{21} \times 100\%$$

$$= \frac{+0 \cdot 5}{21} \times 100\%$$

$$= 2 \cdot 4\% \text{ (correct to one decimal place)}$$

(b) The percentage error

$$= \frac{|21 - 21 \cdot 125|}{21} \times 100\%$$

$$= \frac{+0 \cdot 125}{21} \times 100\%$$

$$= 0 \cdot 6\% \text{ (correct to one decimal place)}$$

(iv) **(b)** gives the more accurate result.

The justification could be that:

(b) had more strips than **(a)** and more strips implies greater accuracy.

It is worth noting that the previous example could
have provided the diagram shown here then asked:

(i) To estimate/measure each vertical height
h_1, h_2, h_3 and h_4 as indicated, where each
vertical division represents 1 m.

(ii) To estimate the shaded area using the
trapezoidal rule with three strips correct to
one decimal place.

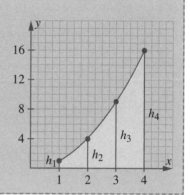

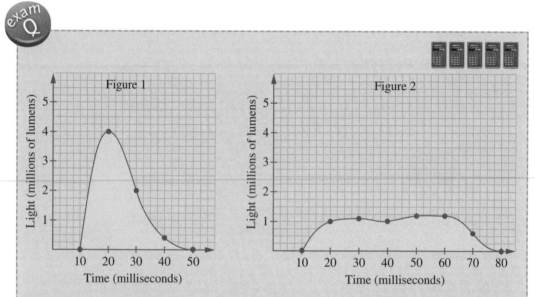

Figure 1

Figure 2

The rate at which flashbulbs give off light varies during the flash.

For some bulbs, the light, measured in lumens, reaches a peak and fades quickly,
as shown in Figure 1.

For other bulbs, the light, instead of reaching a peak, stays at a moderate level for
a relatively longer period of time, as shown in Figure 2.

To calculate how much light reaches the film in a camera, we must know when
the shutter opens and closes. A typical shutter opens 10 milliseconds and closes
60 milliseconds after the button is pressed.

The amount A in lumen-milliseconds of light emitted by the flashbulb is given by
the shaded area under the curve.

Use the trapezoidal rule and the numerical data from Figure 1 and Figure 2 to
estimate A for each of the given bulbs. State which bulb gets more light to the
film. Justify your answer.

This type of question requires you to use the numbers provided from the graphs and the paragraph of text to solve the question. Do not be thrown by the language. Look for the figures that will be useful.

Solution

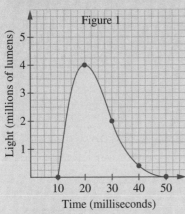

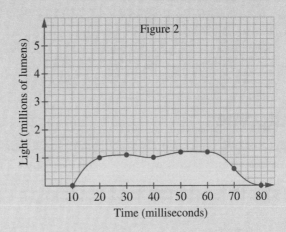

The question gives no instruction/suggestion for the interval widths. Here, each interval width is taken as 10 milliseconds. An interval width of 5 milliseconds would give a more accurate answer.

Reading values of h from Figure 1, we find:

Width = w = 10

$h_1 = 0$	$h_4 = 0·4$
$h_2 = 4$	$h_5 = 0$
$h_3 = 2$	

Area = $\dfrac{w}{2}[h_1 + h_5 + 2(h_2 + h_3 + h_4)]$

$= \dfrac{10}{2}[0 + 0 + 2(4 + 2 + 0·4)]$

$= 5[0 + 12·8]$

$= 64$ lumen-milliseconds

Reading values of h from Figure 2, we find:

Width = w = 10

$h_1 = 0$	$h_5 = 1·2$
$h_2 = 1$	$h_6 = 1·2$
$h_3 = 1·1$	$h_7 = 0·6$
$h_4 = 1$	$h_8 = 0$

Area = $\dfrac{w}{2}[h_1 + h_8 + 2(h_2 + h_3 + h_4$

$+ h_5 + h_6 + h_7)]$

$= \dfrac{10}{2}[0 + 0 + 2(1 + 1·1 + 1$

$+ 1·2 + 1·2 + 0·6)]$

$= 5[0 + 12·2]$

$= 61$ lumen-milliseconds

Hence, we conclude the bulb from Figure 1 gets more light to the film.

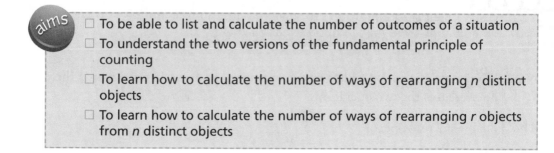

Permutations

Outcomes

The result of an operation is called an outcome. For example, if we throw a die, one possible outcome is 2. If we throw a die there are six possible outcomes: 1, 2, 3, 4, 5 or 6.

Fundamental principle of counting 1

> Suppose one operation has m outcomes and that a second operation has n outcomes. The number of possible outcomes when performing the first operation **followed by** the second operation is $m \times n$.

Performing one operation **and** another operation means we **multiply** the number of possible outcomes.

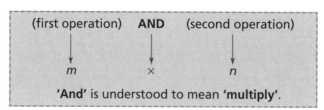

(first operation)   **AND**   (second operation)

m $\times$ n

'And' is understood to mean 'multiply'.

Note: We assume that the outcome of one operation does not affect the number of possible outcomes of the other operation.

The fundamental principle of counting 1 can be extended to three or more operations.

Fundamental principle of counting 2

> Suppose one operation has m outcomes and that a second operation has n outcomes. Then the number of possible outcomes of the first operation **or** the second operation is given by $m + n$.

Performing one operation **or** another operation means we **add** the number of possible outcomes.

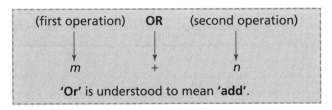

(first operation)	OR	(second operation)
m	$+$	n

'Or' is understood to mean 'add'.

Note: We assume it is not possible for both operations to occur. In other words, there is no overlap of the two operations.

The fundamental principle of counting 2 can be extended to three or more operations, as long as none of the operations overlap.

key point

- **'And'** is understood to mean **'multiply'**.
- **'Or'** is understood to mean **'add'**.

Example

Ciara wants to borrow a book from a friend. Her friend has 12 fiction books and seven non-fiction books. If Ciara can only borrow one book, how many possible outcomes are there for the book she borrows?

Solution

Total number of outcomes = (no. of fiction books) OR (no. of non-fiction books)
Total number of outcomes = (12) + (7)
Total number of outcomes = 19

Example

Sharon wants to buy a dress. The dress is available in sizes small, medium or large and in colours of either blue or red.

(i) How many possible outcomes are there for Sharon's purchase?

(ii) List these outcomes.

Solution

(i) Total number of outcomes = (number of sizes) AND (number of colours)
   Total number of outcomes = (3) × (2)
   Total number of outcomes = 6

(ii) The six possible outcomes are:

Small and blue	Medium and blue	Large and blue
Small and red	Medium and red	Large and red

A restaurant offers an early bird menu, which has three starters, five main courses, four desserts and an option of tea or coffee. How many different ways can you order a meal?

Solution

Total number of ways = (starters) AND (main courses) AND (desserts) AND (drinks)

Total number of ways = (3) × (5) × (4) × (2)

Total number of ways = 120

Colin prints his holiday photographs in a camera shop. The shop can print photographs in sizes small, medium or large, colour or black and white, glossy or matte finish.

(i) How many different ways are there for Colin to print a photograph?

(ii) Colin wants to print all his photos in medium size. How many ways are there for him to print his photos now?

Solution

(i) Total number of ways = (size) AND (colour) AND (finish)

Total number of ways = (3) × (2) × (2)

Total number of ways = 12

key point

'Black and white' counts as only one option.

(ii) Since Colin wants all his photos to be in medium size, then there is only one option for the size.

Total number of ways = (size) AND (colour) AND (finish)

Total number of ways = (1) × (2) × (2)

Total number of ways = 4

There are very few calculations involved with some of these questions, so it is very important that you show the method you used to solve the problem. **In general, the answer alone, with no workings, may not be awarded full marks.**

Permutations (arrangements)

A permutation is a variation or an alternative way of arranging something.

Look out for the word **'arranged'** or **'arrangements'**. This indicates that the question is about **permutations**.

Example

How many ways can the letters of the word CAT be rearranged?

Solution

Draw three boxes. Each box represents a letter: ☐☐☐

Step 1:
Any of the three letters can be placed in the first position, so we have three options for this box.

Step 2:
Now one letter has been used up so there are only two options for the second box.

Step 3:
Two letters have been used up now, so there is only one option for the last box.

| 3 | 2 | 1 |

To find the total number of arrangements, we multiply the numbers in the boxes. The number of arrangements is $3 \times 2 \times 1 = 6$ arrangements.

Factorial function (!)

This is a function on your calculator, which instantly multiplies a number by all the numbers which come before it, down as far as 1.

$5 \times 4 \times 3 \times 2 \times 1 = 5! = 120$

$7 \times 6 \times 5 \times 4 \times 3 \times 2 \times 1 = 7! = 5,040$

Example

Daniel has seven books on his bookshelf. How many ways can he rearrange these books on the shelf?

Solution

Draw seven boxes. Each box represents a book. Put the number of options into each box: 7 options for the first box, then 6 options for the next box, then 5, etc.

7	6	5	4	3	2	1

Number of arrangements = $7 \times 6 \times 5 \times 4 \times 3 \times 2 \times 1 = 7! = 5,040$ arrangements

(i)   How many ways can be the letters of the word BIRTHDAY be rearranged?

(ii) How many four-letter arrangements can be made from the letters of the word BIRTHDAY?

Solution

(i)   Draw eight boxes. Each box represents a letter. Put the number of options into each box: 8 options for the first box, then 7 options for the next box, then 6, etc.

8	7	6	5	4	3	2	1

Number of arrangements = $8 \times 7 \times 6 \times 5 \times 4 \times 3 \times 2 \times 1 = 8! = 40,320$ arrangements.

(ii) Draw four boxes. Each box represents a letter. Put the number of options into each box. BIRTHDAY has eight letters, so there are 8 options for the first box, then 7, etc.

8	7	6	5

Number of arrangements = $8 \times 7 \times 6 \times 5 = 1,680$ arrangements

key point

Permutation function (^nP_r)

This is a function on your calculator that calculates the number of ways r objects can be arranged from n distinct objects.

6 objects permuted in 3 ways: $^6P_3 = 120$

8 objects permuted in 4 ways: $^8P_4 = 1,680$

Restrictions

If there is a restriction on the arrangement, for example the arrangement must begin with a D, put this restriction in first.

Example

How many ways can the letters of the word APRIL be rearranged if the letter P must be in the first position?

Solution

Draw five boxes. Each box represents a letter. We want the arrangement to start with a P, so we have only one option for that box.

Step 1:
The first letter must be P, so there is only one option for this box.

Step 2:
The letter P has been used. There are only four options left for this box, then three, then two, then one.

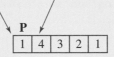

Number of arrangements $= 1 \times 4 \times 3 \times 2 \times 1 = 24$ arrangements

exam focus

It is good practice to draw the boxes and **put the restriction above the box**. This makes it very clear to the examiner where your figures are coming from and the steps you took in reaching your solution.

Example

(i) How many ways can the letters of the word MODERN be rearranged?

(ii) How many of these arrangements end with the letter D?

(iii) How many of these arrangements begin with the letter R and end with the letter D?

(iv) How many of these arrangements end with a vowel?

Solution

(i) Draw six boxes. Each box represents a letter. There are 6 options for the first box, then 5, then 4, etc.

6	5	4	3	2	1

Number of arrangements $= 6 \times 5 \times 4 \times 3 \times 2 \times 1 = 6! = 720$ arrangements

(ii) Draw six boxes. Each box represents a letter. We want the arrangement to end with a D, so we have only one option for that box. Now one letter has been used, so there are only 5 options for the first box, then 4, then 3, etc.

D

5	4	3	2	1	1

Number of arrangements $= 5 \times 4 \times 3 \times 2 \times 1 \times 1 = 120$ arrangements

(iii) Draw six boxes. Each box represents a letter. We want the arrangement to begin with an R and end with a D, so we have only one option for those two boxes. Now two letters have been used, so there are only 4 options for the second box, then 3, then 2, etc.

R   D

1	4	3	2	1	1

Number of arrangements $= 1 \times 4 \times 3 \times 2 \times 1 \times 1 = 24$ arrangements

(iv) Draw six boxes. Each box represents a letter. We want the arrangement to end with a vowel. There are 2 vowels in the word MODERN, so we have two options for the last box. However, only one letter is actually used, so that leaves 5 options for the first box, then 4, then 3, etc.

> **key point**
>
> Vowels are the letters A, E, I, O and U.

vowel

5	4	3	2	1	2

Number of arrangements $= 5 \times 4 \times 3 \times 2 \times 1 \times 2 = 240$ arrangements

(i) Six friends, Amy, Barbara, Conor, David, Emma and Fred, go to the cinema. In how many ways can the six friends be seated in the cinema?

(ii) If Amy and David want to sit beside each other, in how many ways can the six friends be arranged?

(iii) Amy and David have a fight before getting to the cinema, so they will not sit beside each other. In how many ways can the six friends be seated now?

Solution

(i) Draw six boxes. Each box represents a seat. There are 6 options for the first box, then 5, then 4, etc.

6	5	4	3	2	1

Number of arrangements = 6 × 5 × 4 × 3 × 2 × 1 = 6! = 720 arrangements

(ii) If Amy and David want to sit together, we must consider them to be one object and so there are now only five objects to be rearranged: (AD), B, C, E, F.

5	4	3	2	1

Number of arrangements = 5 × 4 × 3 × 2 × 1 = 5! = 120 arrangements

However, Amy and David can be seated in two ways: as Amy and David or David and Amy, so we must multiply all of the arrangements by 2.

So, total number or arrangements = 120 × 2 = 240 ways that Amy and David can be seated beside each other.

(iii) If Amy and David do not want to sit beside each other, then we want all arrangements, except the ones where Amy and David **are** beside each other.

Number of arrangements with Amy and David apart

= all arrangements − (number of arrangements where Amy and David are together)

Number of arrangements with Amy and David apart = 720 − 240 = 480

(i) A number plate consists of four letters of the English alphabet and two digits. If no letter or digit can be repeated and 0 can never be used as the first digit, how many different plates can be manufactured?

FXRA 87

(for example)

(ii) A number plate consists of four digits and two letters of the English alphabet. If no letter or digit can be repeated and 0 can never be used as the first digit, how many different plates can be manufactured?

8603 PL

(for example)

(iii) Ireland is considering changing its vehicle license plates to one of the above options. Which option would you recommend? Give a reason for your answer.

key point

Remember:

There are 26 letters in the English alphabet.

There are 10 digits:

0, 1, 2, 3, 4, 5, 6, 7, 8, 9

Solution

(i) Draw six boxes. The first four are for the letters and the last two are for the digits. There are 26 letters in the alphabet, so there are 26 options for the first box, then 25, etc.

The first digit cannot be 0, so there are only 9 options for that box. Now one digit has been used, but we can use 0 in the second position, so there are 9 options for that box too.

Letters				Digits	
26	25	24	23	9	9

Number of license plates = 26 × 25 × 24 × 23 × 9 × 9 = 29,062,800 license plates

(ii) Draw six boxes. The first four are for the digits and the last two are for the letters. The first digit cannot be 0, so there are only 9 options for the first box, now one digit has been used, but we can use 0 in the second position, so there are 9 options for the second box, then 8, etc.

There are 26 letters of the alphabet, so there are 26 options for the first box, then 25.

Digits				Letters	
9	9	8	7	26	25

Number of license plates = 9 × 9 × 8 × 7 × 26 × 25 = 2,948,400 license plates

(iii) In my opinion, Ireland should use the option in part **(i)**, as this option allows the country to have over 29 million license plates before they run out.

OR

In my opinion, Ireland should use the option in part **(ii)**, as there are fewer than 2 million registered vehicles in Ireland and so the option in part **(ii)** allows for enough licenses.

Remember, there is no single correct answer to this opinion type of question. So long as your answer is logical and plausible, you should get the marks.

(2015 Q.1)

A bank issues a unique six-digit password to each of its online customers. The password may contain any of numbers 0 to 9 in any position and numbers may be repeated. For example, the following it a valid password.

0	7	1	7	3	7

(a) How many different passwords are possible?

(b) **(i)** How many different passwords do **not** contain **any** zero?

   (ii) One password is selected at random from all the possible passwords. What is the probability that this password contains at least one zero?

(c) John is issued with one such password from the bank. Each time John wants to access his account online, the bank's website requires him to input three of his password digits into the boxes provided. For example, he may be asked for the 1st, 3rd and 6th digits, as shown below.

*		*			*

In how many different ways can the bank select the three required boxes?

Solution

(a) There are 10 digits to choose from, with no restrictions and repetition is allowed:

10	10	10	10	10	10

Number of possible passwords = $10 \times 10 \times 10 \times 10 \times 10 \times 10$
= 10^6 = 1,000,000

(b) **(i)** Leaving out zero, there are now 9 digits to choose from, with no restrictions and repetition is allowed:

9	9	9	9	9	9

Number of possible passwords = $9 \times 9 \times 9 \times 9 \times 9 \times 9 = 9^6 = 531,441$

(ii) P(at least one zero) = 1 − P(no zero)

$$= 1 - \frac{531441}{1000000}$$

$$= \frac{468559}{1000000} = 0{\cdot}468559$$

(c) We can systematically list all possible options for selecting 3 digits from 6:

123, 124, 125, 126, 134, 135, 136, 145, 146, 156,

234, 235, 236, 245, 246, 256, 345, 346, 356, 456

Therefore, there are 20 different ways the bank can select the three required boxes.

Five friends, Alan, Brian, Conor, David and Eoin, go to a restaurant and sit at a round table.

How many ways can the five friends be arranged around the table?

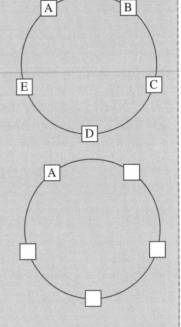

Solution

If the friends were sitting in a straight line, then the ways of arranging them would be 5!

However, because they are seated in a circle, this would result in repeated arrangements.

The key to arranging objects in a circle is to have one object fixed and then rearrange all the other objects around the table.

So in this problem, put Alan in a fixed position and then rearrange Brian, Conor, David and Eoin.

Rearranging B, C, D and E is calculated as 4! = 24.

Thus, there are 24 ways in which the friends can be rearranged around the table.

The number of ways to rearrange n objects in a line is found by n!.

The number of ways to rearrange n objects in a circle is found by $(n − 1)!$.

10 Probability

aims

- [ ] To know that the probability of an event occurring must be between 0 and 1
- [ ] To learn how to calculate the probability of an event occurring
- [ ] To learn how to use venn diagrams, sample spaces and tree diagrams in finding all possible outcomes and probabilities
- [ ] To understand when and how to use Bernoulli Trials
- [ ] To calculate the expected value of an event

Introduction

Probability involves the study of the laws of chance. It is a measure of the chance, or likelihood, of something happening.

If you carry out an operation, or experiment, using coins, dice, spinners or cards, then each toss, throw, spin or draw is called a **trial**. The possible things that can happen from a trial are called **outcomes**. The outcomes of interest are called an **event**. In other words, an event is the set of successful outcomes.

> **key point**
>
> You need to understand all the words in bold print: **probability, trial, outcome, event**

For example, if you throw a die and you are interested in the probability of throwing an even number, then the event is 2, 4, 6 – the successful outcomes.

If E is an event, then $P(E)$ stands for the probability that the event occurs. $P(E)$ is read as 'the probability of E'.

The probability of an event is a number between 0 and 1, including 0 and 1.

$$0 \leq P(E) \leq 1$$

The value of $P(E)$ can be given as a fraction, decimal or percentage.

Note: $P(E) = 0$ means that an event is **impossible**.

$P(E) = 1$ means that an event is **certain**.

The chance of an event happening can be shown on a **probability scale**:

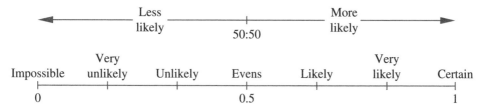

The measure of the probability of an event, *E*, is given by:

$$P(E) = \frac{\text{Number of successful outcomes}}{\text{Number of possible outcomes}}$$

key point

You must be able to calculate the probability of an event happening on a scale from 0 to 1.

Example

The probability of four events have been marked on a probability scale.

Event *P* : A person is over 4 metres tall.

Event *Q* : A fair coin lands tails up.

Event *R* : Getting a score less than 7 on one roll of a fair 6-sided die.

Event *S* : Pick a number at random greater than 1 from 1, 2, 3 and 4.

Label the arrows with the letters *P*, *Q*, *R* and *S* to show the event they represent.

Solution

Determine the probability of each event.

Event *P*: A person is over 4 metres tall.

The tallest man on Earth is approximately 2·7 metres tall, so it is not possible for a person to be 4 metres tall. Therefore, the probability of Event *P* occurring is 0.

Event *Q*: A fair coin lands tails up.

A coin has two faces, head and tails, and it is equally likely to land on either of them. Therefore, the probability of Event *Q* occurring is 0·5.

Event *R*: Getting a score less than 7 on one roll of a fair 6-sided die.

All values on a die are less than 7, so it is a certainty that the die will land on a number less than 7. Therefore, the probability of Event *R* occurring is 1.

Event *S*: Pick a number at random greater than 1 from 1, 2, 3 and 4.

There are three numbers greater than 1, so there is a 3 out of 4 chance of selecting a number greater than 1. Therefore, the probability of Event *S* occurring is $\frac{3}{4} = 0·75$.

Put these probabilities on the scale:

Example

(i) One hundred and fifty students sitting an examination were grouped according to age (16, 17 or 18) and gender (female or male). The results are given in the following table:

	Age 16	Age 17	Age 18	Total
Female	30	18	12	60
Male	60	27	3	90

One student is chosen at random. What is the probability that the student is:
(a) Male (b) A 16-year-old female (c) Younger than 18 (d) Older than 19

(ii) Label the probability of each event with the letters A, B, C and D, respectively. Indicate the position of A, B, C and D on the probability scale.

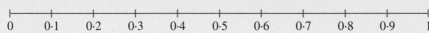

Solution

(i) (a) $P(\text{male}) = \dfrac{\text{Number of males}}{\text{Total number of people}}$

$P(\text{male}) = \dfrac{90}{150}$

$P(\text{male}) = \dfrac{3}{5} = 0.6$

(b) $P(\text{16-yr-old female}) = \dfrac{\text{Number of 16-yr-old females}}{\text{Total number of people}}$

$P(\text{16-yr-old female}) = \dfrac{30}{150}$

$P(\text{16-yr-old female}) = \dfrac{1}{5} = 0.2$

(c) $P(\text{younger than } 18) = \dfrac{\text{Number of people younger than } 18}{\text{Total number of people}}$

$P(\text{younger than } 18) = \dfrac{135}{150}$

$P(\text{younger than } 18) = \dfrac{9}{10} = 0{\cdot}9$

(d) $P(\text{older than } 19) = \dfrac{\text{Number of people older than } 19}{\text{Total number of people}}$

$P(\text{older than } 19) = \dfrac{0}{150}$

$P(\text{older than } 19) = 0$

(ii) Labelling the answers from (a), (b), (c) and (d) on the probability scale:

```
     D            B                              A                    C
     ├──┬────┬────┬────┬────┬────┬────┬────┬────┬────┬──┤
     0  0·1  0·2  0·3  0·4  0·5  0·6  0·7  0·8  0·9   1
```

Example

(i) A bag contains three red, three green and four blue marbles. A marble is selected at random from the bag. What is the probability of selecting a blue marble?

(ii) The selected marble is to be put back into the bag, plus a certain number of red marbles. This causes the probability of selecting a red marble to be equal to $\frac{1}{2}$. Find the number of extra red marbles that were placed in the bag.

Solution

(i) $P(\text{blue marble}) = \dfrac{\text{Number of blue marbles}}{\text{Total number of marbles}}$

$P(\text{blue marble}) = \dfrac{4}{10} = \dfrac{2}{5}$

(ii) Let the number of red marbles added be x:

$P(\text{red marble}) = \dfrac{\text{Number of red marbles}}{\text{Total number of marbles}}$

$\dfrac{1}{2} = \dfrac{3 + x}{10 + x}$

$(10 + x)(1) = (2)(3 + x)$

$10 + x = 6 + 2x$

key point

'Drawn at random' means that every item is equally likely to be drawn.

$$10 - 6 = 2x - x$$
$$4 = x$$

Therefore, 4 red marbles were added to the bag.

This problem could also have been solved using trial and improvement instead of algebra.

exam
Q

(2013 Q.1)

Katie tossed a coin 200 times and threw 109 heads. Joe tossed the same coin 400 times and threw 238 heads. Lucy tossed the same coin 500 times and threw 291 heads. Katie, Joe and Lucy now think the coin may be biased.

(a) Give a reason why they think that the coin may be biased.

(b) Lucy uses all the above data and calculates that the best estimate of the probability of throwing a head with this coin is 0·58. Show how Lucy might have calculated this probability.

(c) Joe agrees with Lucy's estimate of 0·58 as the probability of throwing a head with this coin. He claims that the probability of throwing 3 successive heads with this coin is less than the probability of throwing 2 successive tails. Calculate the probability of each event and state whether Joe's claim is true or not.

Solution

(a) The probability of throwing a head for each person is as follows:

Katie: $\dfrac{109}{200} = 0\cdot545$;　　Joe: $\dfrac{238}{400} = 0\cdot595$;　　Lucy: $\dfrac{291}{500} = 0\cdot582$

In each case the probability of throwing a head was greater than 0·5 or 50%, which would lead you to believe that the coin is biased.

(b) $P(\text{head}) = \dfrac{\text{Total number of heads}}{\text{Total number of tosses}}$

$$= \frac{109 + 238 + 291}{200 + 400 + 500} = \frac{638}{1100} = 0\cdot58$$

(c) P(3 heads) = 0·58 × 0·58 × 0·58 = 0·195112

P(2 tails) = 0·42 × 0·42 = 0·1764

The probability of throwing two tails is less than the probability of throwing three heads, therefore Joe's claim is incorrect.

There are 80 members in a club: 32 male and 48 female. Four of the males and eight of the females wear glasses. A club member is selected at random.

(i) What is the probability that the club member is a:

    (a) Male   **(b)** Person wearing glasses   **(c)** Female not wearing glasses.

(ii) A male from the club is selected at random.
What is the probability that he wears glasses?

(iii) A member who wears glasses is selected at random.
What is the probability that it is a female?

(iv) All members who wear glasses resign from the club. What is the probability that a club member now selected at random is female?

Solution

(i) (a) $P(\text{male}) = \dfrac{\text{Number of males}}{\text{Total number of people}} = \dfrac{32}{80} = \dfrac{2}{5}$

    (b) $P(\text{wearing glasses}) = \dfrac{\text{Number of people wearing glasses}}{\text{Total number of people}} = \dfrac{12}{80} = \dfrac{3}{20}$

    (c) $P(\text{female and no glasses}) = \dfrac{\text{Number of females with no glasses}}{\text{Total number of people}} = \dfrac{40}{80} = \dfrac{1}{2}$

(ii) A male is selected, so we will only consider the males when working out the probabilities.

$$P(\text{wearing glasses}) = \frac{\text{Number of males wearing glasses}}{\text{Total number of males}} = \frac{4}{32} = \frac{1}{8}$$

(iii) A person wearing glasses is selected, so we will only consider the people with glasses when working out the probabilities.

$$P(\text{female}) = \frac{\text{Number of females wearing glasses}}{\text{Total number of people wearing glasses}} = \frac{8}{12} = \frac{2}{3}$$

(iv) All members with glasses leave, so now there are only 28 males and 40 females.

$$P(\text{male}) = \frac{\text{Number of males}}{\text{Total number of members}} = \frac{28}{68} = \frac{7}{17}$$

Deck of cards:

There are **52 cards** in a deck of cards.

4 suits: **Red: hearts** and **diamonds**

   Black: clubs and **spades**

Each suit has 13 cards: Ace, 2, 3, 4, 5, 6, 7, 8, 9, 10, Jack, Queen and King.

The Jack, Queen and King are known as 'picture cards'.

Die (dice for more than one):

A 6-sided die is a cube with dots on each side.
The dots represent numbers from 1 to 6.
The numbers on the opposite sides of a die add up to 7.
A fair die is equally likely to land on any of the numbers from 1 to 6.

Note: A die does not necessarily only have 6 sides, it is possible to have die with more or fewer sides than 6.

Addition rule

The addition rule is often called the **or rule**. It is important to remember that $P(A$ or $B)$ means A occurs or B occurs or both occur. By subtracting $P(A$ and $B)$, the possibility of double counting is removed.

> The probability that two events, A or B, can happen is given by:
>
> $$P(A \text{ or } B) = P(A) + P(B) - P(A \text{ and } B)$$
>
> (removes double counting)

Probability of an event not happening

If E is any event, then 'not E' is the event that E does not occur. Clearly, E and not E cannot occur at the same time. Either E or not E must occur. Thus, we have the following relationship between the probabilities of E and not E:

$$P(E) + P(\text{not } E) = 1$$

or

$$P(\text{not } E) = 1 - P(E)$$

Note: $P(\text{not } E)$ can also be written as $P(\bar{E})$ or $P(E')$

Example

In the Lotto, there are 45 numbers, numbered from 1 to 45. Find the probability that the first number drawn is:

(i) A number divisible by 6 or 4

(ii) Not a number divisible by 6 or a 4.

Solution

(i) The numbers which are divisible by 6 are: 6, 12, 18, 24, 30, 36, 42.
   The numbers which are divisible by 4 are: 4, 8, 12, 16, 20, 24, 28, 32, 36, 40, 44.
   The numbers which are divisible by both 6 and 4 are: 12, 24, 36.
   $P(\text{divisible by 6 or 4}) = P(\text{divisible by 6}) + P(\text{divisible by 4}) - P(\text{divisible by 6 and 4})$

$$P(\text{divisible by 6 or 4}) = \frac{7}{45} + \frac{11}{45} - \frac{3}{45}$$

$$P(\text{divisible by 6 or 4}) = \frac{15}{45}$$

$$P(\text{divisible by 6 or 4}) = \frac{1}{3}$$

key point

$$P(A \text{ or } B) = P(A) + P(B) - P(A \text{ and } B)$$

(ii) $P(\text{not divisible by 6 or 4}) = 1 - P(\text{divisible by 6 or 4})$

$$P(\text{not divisible by 6 or 4}) = 1 - \frac{1}{3}$$

$$P(\text{not divisible by 6 or 4}) = \frac{2}{3}$$

key point

$$P(\text{not } E) = 1 - P(E)$$

A pack of cards contains 52 cards. A card is drawn at random. Find:

(i) The probability it is a picture card

(ii) The probability it is a club or a Queen

(iii) The probability it is not a club or a Queen.

Solution

(i) $P(\text{picture card}) = \dfrac{\text{Number of picture cards}}{\text{Total number of cards}} = \dfrac{12}{52} = \dfrac{3}{13}$

(ii) $P(\text{club or Queen}) = P(\text{club}) + P(\text{Queen}) - P(\text{club and Queen})$

$P(\text{club or Queen}) = \dfrac{13}{52} + \dfrac{4}{52} - \dfrac{1}{52}$

$P(\text{club or Queen}) = \dfrac{16}{52}$

$P(\text{club or Queen}) = \dfrac{4}{13}$

Note: Question **(ii)** could also have been solved by observation. When you study a deck of cards, you can see that if you count all the clubs and all the Queens, the Queen of clubs falls into both categories. As you can see from the diagram below, there are 16 cards which are clubs **or** Queens.

Thus, $P(\text{club or Queen}) = \dfrac{16}{52} = \dfrac{4}{13}$

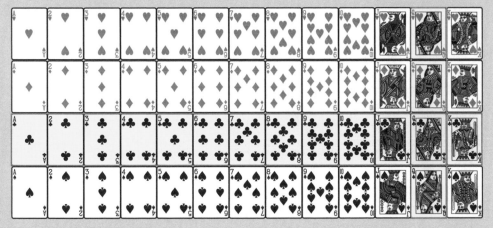

(iii) $P(\text{not club or Queen}) = 1 - P(\text{club or Queen})$

$P(\text{not club or Queen}) = 1 - \dfrac{4}{13}$

$P(\text{not club or Queen}) = \dfrac{9}{13}$

(2014 Q.1)

A garage has 5 black cars, 9 red cars and 10 silver cars for sale.

(a) A car is selected at random. What is the probability that
  (i) The car is black?
  (ii) The car is black or red?

(b) A car is selected at random. Then a second car is selected at random from those remaining. What is the probability that:
  (i) The first car is silver and the second car is black?
  (ii) One of the selected cars is red and the other is black?

(c) Three of the black cars, two of the red cars and four of the silver cars have diesel engines. One car from the garage is again selected at random. What is the probability that it is a red car or a diesel car?

Solution

(a) (i) $P(\text{black}) = \dfrac{\text{Number of black}}{\text{Total number of cars}} = \dfrac{5}{24}$

  (ii) $P(\text{black or red}) = \dfrac{\text{Number of black and red}}{\text{Total number of cars}} = \dfrac{14}{24} = \dfrac{7}{12}$

(b) (i) $P(\text{first silver, second black}) = \dfrac{10}{24} \times \dfrac{5}{23} = \dfrac{25}{276}$

  (ii) $P(\text{first red, second black})$ or $P(\text{first black, second red})$

  $$= \left(\dfrac{9}{24} \times \dfrac{5}{23}\right) + \left(\dfrac{5}{24} \times \dfrac{9}{23}\right) = \dfrac{15}{184} + \dfrac{15}{184} = \dfrac{15}{92}$$

(c) $P(\text{red or diesel}) = P(\text{red}) + P(\text{diesel}) - P(\text{red and diesel})$

  $$= \dfrac{9}{24} + \dfrac{9}{24} - \dfrac{2}{24}$$

  $$= \dfrac{16}{24} = \dfrac{2}{3}$$

Venn diagram

Some situations can be presented clearly in a Venn diagram. This can then make it easier to work out the probabilities.

(2012 Q.2)

(i) In the Venn diagram, the universal set is a normal deck of 52 playing cards. The two sets shown represent clubs and picture cards (Kings, Queens and Jacks).

Show on the diagram the number of elements in each region.

Clubs   Picture cards

[ ]   [ ]   [ ]

[ ]

(ii) (a) A card is drawn from a pack of 52 cards. Find the probability that the card drawn is the King of clubs.

(b) A card is drawn from a pack of 52 cards. Find the probability that the card drawn is a club or a picture card.

(c) Two cards are drawn from a pack of 52 cards. Find the probability that neither of them is a club or a picture card. Give your answer correct to two decimal places.

Solution

(i) There are 13 clubs in the pack.

There are 12 picture cards in the pack. Three of the clubs are picture cards, so the intersection is 3.

That leaves 10 cards in the clubs set and nine cards in the picture cards set.

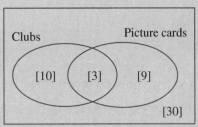

We have now entered 22 cards into the diagram, so there are 30 cards in the universal set on the outside.

(ii) (a) There is only one King of clubs in a pack of 52 cards, so there is only one favourable outcome:

$$P(\text{King of clubs}) = \frac{\text{Number of favourable outcomes}}{\text{Total number of cards}} = \frac{1}{52}$$

(b) There are 13 clubs and 12 picture cards. However, there are three cards which are both a club and a picture, so we cannot count these twice.

Therefore, the number of favourable outcomes $= 13 + 12 - 3 = 22$.

$$P(\text{club or picture card}) = \frac{\text{Number of favourable outcomes}}{\text{Total number of cards}} = \frac{22}{52} = \frac{11}{26}$$

Note: You could also have used the Venn diagram to count the number of clubs and picture cards.

(c) We treat this problem as though one card is removed from the pack and **not replaced**, then another card is drawn from the remaining 51 cards:

$$P(\text{not a club or a picture card}) = P(1^{st} \text{ card drawn}) \text{ and } P(2^{nd} \text{ card drawn})$$

$$P(\text{not a club or a picture card}) = \frac{30}{52} \times \frac{29}{51} = 0.328 = 0.33$$

Sample space

A sample space is the set of all possible outcomes. A sample space can be very useful for seeing all possible outcomes and working out any appropriate probabilities.

A game consists of two spinners: one with four segments numbered 1 to 4, and the second with five segments numbered 1 to 5. The spinners are spun.

 (i) Draw a sample space of all possible outcomes.

 (ii) If the spinners are fair, what is the probability of getting two 4s?

(iii) If the spinners are fair, what is the probability the values on the spinners sum to 6?

(iv) Jason thinks that one of the spinners is not fair.

Describe an experiment that he could do to find out whether the spinner is fair.

Solution

(i) Sample space showing all possible outcomes:

		Spinner 1			
		1	2	3	4
Spinner 2	1	1, 1			1, 4
	2		2, 2		
	3				3, 4
	4	4, 1		4, 3	
	5				5, 4

key point

The numbers in the grid represent all the possible outcomes. A few have been filled in for you to understand what the grid represents. The total number of outcomes is 5 × 4 = 20.

(ii) There is only one outcome in which **both** spinners land on 4:

$$P(\text{both spinners land on 4}) = \frac{\text{Number of favourable outcomes}}{\text{Total number of outcomes}} = \frac{1}{20}$$

(iii) Use the same space to determine which outcomes will give a sum of 6. These are shaded in the grid.

$$P(\text{sum of six}) = \frac{\text{Number where sum is 6}}{\text{Total number of outcomes}}$$

$$P(\text{sum of six}) = \frac{4}{20}$$

$$P(\text{sum of six}) = \frac{1}{5}$$

		Spinner 1			
		1	2	3	4
Spinner 2	1				
	2				2, 4
	3			3, 3	
	4		4, 2		
	5	5, 1			

(iv) Jason should spin the spinner he thinks is not fair a very large number of times and record the number it lands on. If the spinner is fair, it should land on each number, from 1 to 4, approximately the same number of times. That is, it should land on each number approximately one-quarter of the time.

Tree diagrams

We can also construct a probability tree diagram to help us solve some probability problems. A probability tree diagram shows all the possible outcomes.

key point

To calculate the probability along a path, you multiply all probabilities along the branches on that path.

Example

A bowl of fruit contains eight apples and four bananas.

(i) Jake chooses a piece of fruit at random. Find the probability that he chooses an apple.

(ii) Jake chooses a piece of fruit and eats it. He then chooses a 2nd piece of fruit.

    (a) Draw a tree diagram to show all possible outcomes for the pieces of fruit Jake can select.

    (b) Use the tree diagram to find the probability that Jake chooses an apple followed by a banana.

Solution

(i) $P(\text{apple}) = \dfrac{\text{Number of apples}}{\text{Total number of fruit}}$

    $P(\text{apple}) = \dfrac{8}{12} = \dfrac{2}{3}$

(ii) (a) Tree diagram:

    Where A = apple and B = banana.

    (b) Put the appropriate probabilities on each branch of the tree.

    After the first choice, there will only be 11 pieces of fruit in the bowl.

    If an apple is selected first, there are only seven apples left to choose out of 11 pieces. The probability of selecting an apple after one apple has already been selected is $\frac{7}{11}$.

    Apply this same logic to all branches, to work out each probability.

    Using the tree diagram, we see:

    $P(\text{apple and banana}) = \dfrac{8}{12} \times \dfrac{4}{11}$

    $P(\text{apple and banana}) = \dfrac{32}{132} = \dfrac{8}{33}$

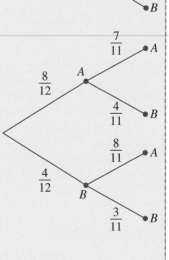

Example

Roisin is taking her driving test.

The test is in two parts: Theory and Practical.

To get her driving license, she has to pass *both* parts of the test.

The probability that Roisin will pass the Theory is 0·9.

The probability that she will pass the Practical is 0·8.

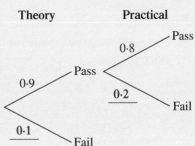

If she fails her Theory she cannot take the Practical.

(i) Complete the tree diagram.

(ii) Calculate the probability that Roisin fails the driving test.

Solution

(i) **Theory exam:**

The probability that Roisin passes the Theory exam is 0·9, so the probability that she fails the Theory exam is $1 - 0·9 = 0·1$.

Practical exam:

The probability that Roisin passes the Practical exam is 0·8, so the probability that she fails the Practical exam is $1 - 0·8 = 0·2$.

(ii) There are two ways in which Roisin can fail the driving test.

(fail the Theory exam) or (pass the Theory exam and then fail the Practical exam)

$P(\text{fail}) = P(\text{fail Theory exam}) + P(\text{pass Theory exam and fail Practical exam})$

$P(\text{fail}) = 0·1 + (0·9 \times 0·2)$

$P(\text{fail}) = 0·1 + 0·18$

$P(\text{fail}) = 0·28$

$\boxed{\text{or}}$

$P(\text{fail}) = 1 - P(\text{pass})$

$P(\text{fail}) = 1 - (0·9 \times 0·8)$

$P(\text{fail}) = 1 - 0·72$

$P(\text{fail}) = 0·28$

(2012 Q.1)

Peter and Niamh go to a large school. One morning, they arrive early. While they are waiting, they decide to guess whether each of the next three students to come in the door will be a boy or a girl.

 (i) Write out the sample space showing all the possible outcomes. For example, BGG is one outcome, representing Boy, Girl, Girl.

 (ii) Peter says these outcomes are equally likely. Niamh says they are not. What do you need to know about the students in the school to decide which of them is correct?

(iii) If all the outcomes are equally likely, what is the probability that the three students will be two girls followed by a boy?

(iv) Niamh guesses that there will be at least one girl among the next three students. Peter guesses that the next three students will be either three boys or two boys and a girl.

Who is more likely to be correct, assuming all outcomes are equally likely? Justify your answer.

Solution

 (i) List out all of the possible outcomes.

   BBB, BBG, BGB, BGG,

   GBB, GBG, GGB, GGG

   Alternatively, you can use a tree diagram to work out all the outcomes.

 (ii) These outcomes are equally likely *only* if there are equal numbers of boys and girls in the school, so we would need to know the total number of boys and girls in the school.

(iii) One outcome out of eight is two girls followed by a boy.

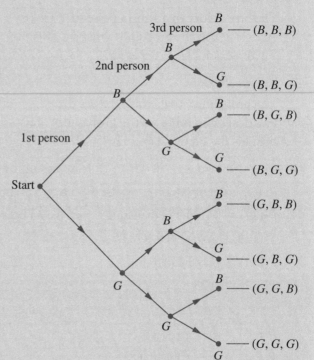

$$P(G, G, B) = \frac{\text{Number of favourable outcomes}}{\text{Total number of outcomes}} = \frac{1}{8}$$

(iv) Niamh guesses there will be **at least** one girl. This means all options, except the one with three boys, so that is seven out of the eight options:

$$P(\text{At least one girl}) = \frac{7}{8}$$

Peter guesses there will be three boys or two boys and a girl, so his options are *BBB, BBG, BGB, GBB*. Each of these options are one outcome out of eight, so:

$$P[(BBB) \text{ or } (GBB) \text{ or } (BGB) \text{ or } (BBG)] = P(BBB) + P(GBB) + P(BGB) + P(BBG)]$$

$$P[(BBB) \text{ or } (GBB) \text{ or } (BGB) \text{ or } (BBG)] = \frac{1}{8} + \frac{1}{8} + \frac{1}{8} + \frac{1}{8}$$

$$P[(BBB) \text{ or } (GBB) \text{ or } (BGB) \text{ or } (BBG)] = \frac{4}{8}$$

It is more likely that Niamh is correct, as her probability is $\frac{7}{8}$ while Peter's probability is only $\frac{4}{8}$.

Alex and Bobby are running in the final of a 100-metre race and a 200-metre race.

The probabilities of each of them winning each race are given in the table below.

The probability that neither of them wins the 100-metre race is also given.

	Alex	Bobby	Neither
100-metre race	$\frac{1}{6}$	$\frac{1}{4}$	$\frac{7}{12}$
200-metre race	$\frac{1}{4}$	$\frac{3}{8}$	

(i) Complete the table by inserting the probability that neither Alex nor Bobby wins the 200-metre race.

(ii) Use a tree diagram to complete a list of all possible outcomes. For example, the outcome that Alex wins the first race and the second race is recorded as (*A, A*).

Write the probability of each outcome.

(iii) What is the probability that Alex and Bobby win one race each?

Solution

(i) The sum of all the probabilities for all three outcomes of the 200-metre race, must add up to 1.

$$\therefore \quad P(\text{neither}) = 1 - \frac{1}{4} - \frac{3}{8}$$

$$P(\text{neither}) = \frac{3}{8}$$

	Alex	Bobby	Neither
100-metre race	$\frac{1}{6}$	$\frac{1}{4}$	$\frac{7}{12}$
200-metre race	$\frac{1}{4}$	$\frac{3}{8}$	$\frac{3}{8}$

(ii) Tree diagram:

The first branches represent the outcomes from the 100-metre race. Following each of these outcomes, we add another set of branches which represent the three possible outcomes for the 200-metre race.

Write the probabilities along each of the branches.

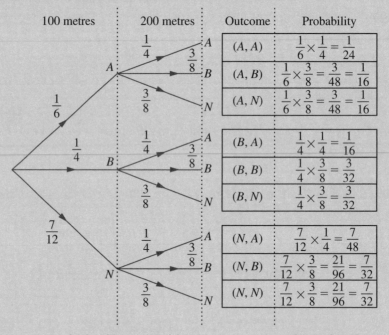

Outcome	Probability
(A, A)	$\frac{1}{6} \times \frac{1}{4} = \frac{1}{24}$
(A, B)	$\frac{1}{6} \times \frac{3}{8} = \frac{3}{48} = \frac{1}{16}$
(A, N)	$\frac{1}{6} \times \frac{3}{8} = \frac{3}{48} = \frac{1}{16}$
(B, A)	$\frac{1}{4} \times \frac{1}{4} = \frac{1}{16}$
(B, B)	$\frac{1}{4} \times \frac{3}{8} = \frac{3}{32}$
(B, N)	$\frac{1}{4} \times \frac{3}{8} = \frac{3}{32}$
(N, A)	$\frac{7}{12} \times \frac{1}{4} = \frac{7}{48}$
(N, B)	$\frac{7}{12} \times \frac{3}{8} = \frac{21}{96} = \frac{7}{32}$
(N, N)	$\frac{7}{12} \times \frac{3}{8} = \frac{21}{96} = \frac{7}{32}$

(iii) The outcomes in which Alex and Bobby win one race each are (A, B) and (B, A).

$$P((A, B) \text{ or } (B, A)) = P(A, B) + P(B, A)$$

$$P((A, B) \text{ or } (B, A)) = \frac{1}{16} + \frac{1}{16}$$

$$P((A, B) \text{ or } (B, A)) = \frac{2}{16}$$

$$P((A, B) \text{ or } (B, A)) = \frac{1}{8}$$

Bernoulli Trials

A Bernoulli Trial is an event in which there are exactly two outcomes: success and failure. Every time the event occurs, the probability of success is the same. If the event is run multiple times, the probability of having a certain number of successes and a certain number of failures can be found by using the following formula:

$$P(r \text{ successes in } n \text{ trials}) = \binom{n}{r} (P(\text{success}))^r (P(\text{failure}))^{n-r}$$

(2014 Q.2)

When taking a penalty kick, the probability that Kevin scores is always $\frac{3}{4}$.

(a) Kevin takes a penalty. What is the probability that he does **not** score?

(b) Kevin takes two penalties. What is the probability that he scores both?

(c) Kevin takes three penalties. What is the probability that he scores exactly twice?

(d) Kevin takes five penalties. What is the probability that he scores for the first time on his fifth penalty?

Solution

(a) $P(\text{not score}) = 1 - P(\text{score})$

$$= 1 - \frac{3}{4} = \frac{1}{4}$$

(b) $P(\text{two scores}) = \frac{3}{4} \times \frac{3}{4} = \frac{9}{16}$

(c) For Kevin to score exactly twice, he must miss one out of the three penalties.

$$P(\text{two scores out of three}) = \binom{3}{2} (P(\text{score}))^2 \times (P(\text{not score}))^1$$

$$= \binom{3}{2}\left(\frac{3}{4}\right)^2 \left(\frac{1}{4}\right)^1$$

$$= 3\left(\frac{9}{16}\right)\left(\frac{1}{4}\right)$$

$$= \frac{27}{64}$$

(d) $P(\text{first score on fifth kick}) = 4 \text{ misses and then 1 score}$

$$= \frac{1}{4} \times \frac{1}{4} \times \frac{1}{4} \times \frac{1}{4} \times \frac{3}{4}$$

$$= \frac{3}{1024}$$

Expected value

When considering the average outcome of an experiment, the mean value, μ, is often called the expected value and is written as $E(x)$.

To calculate the expected value, multiply every possible outcome by the probability for that outcome occurring and then add these values together.

$$E(x) = \sum xP(x)$$

Note: $E(x)$ does not have to be an actual outcome.

Example

A charity got a license to run a raffle. There is one grand prize of €20,000 and 20 additional prizes of €500. Tickets cost €10. Ten thousand tickets were sold for this raffle. Sheila bought one of these tickets.

(i) Calculate the probability that Sheila wins:

    (a) The grand prize   (b) A €500 prize   (c) No prize.

(ii) Calculate the expected value.

(iii) Is this a good bet? Justify your answer.

Solution

(i) (a) $P(\text{winning grand prize}) = \dfrac{\text{Number of grand prize-winning tickets}}{\text{Total number of tickets}}$

         $P(\text{winning grand prize}) = \dfrac{1}{10,000}$

    (b) $P(\text{winning €500 prize}) = \dfrac{\text{Number of €500-winning tickets}}{\text{Total number of tickets}}$

         $P(\text{winning €500 prize}) = \dfrac{20}{10,000} = \dfrac{1}{500}$

    (c) $P(\text{no prize}) = \dfrac{\text{Number of losing tickets}}{\text{Total number of tickets}}$

         $P(\text{no prize}) = \dfrac{9,979}{10,000}$

(ii) Expected value, $E(x) = \sum xP(x)$:

1. Multiply the probability of obtaining each prize $P(x)$ by the prize, x, to get $xP(x)$.

2. Sum all of the $xP(x)$ to find $E(x)$.

From the table, we find $E(x) = €3$. This means that the average value you can expect to win is €3.

Prize (x)	Probability P(x)	xP(x)
€20,000	$\dfrac{1}{10,000}$	€2
€500	$\dfrac{1}{500}$	€1
€0	$\dfrac{9,979}{10,000}$	€0
	$\sum xP(x) =$	€3

(iii) This is not a good bet, as a ticket costs €10. However, the expected value to win is only €3, so on average each raffle ticket will lose €7.

exam
Q

A biased die is used in a game. The probabilities of getting the six different numbers on the die are shown in the table below:

Number	1	2	3	4	5	6
Probability	0·25	0·25	0·15	0·15	0·1	0·1

(i) Find the expected value of the random variable x, where x is the number thrown.

(ii) There is a game at a funfair. It costs €3 to play the game. The player rolls a die once and wins back the number of Euros shown on the die. The sentence below describes the difference between using the above biased die and using a fair (unbiased) die when playing this game. By doing the calculations required, complete the sentence: 'If you play the game many times with a fair die, you will win an average of _____ per game, but if you play with the biased die you will lose an average of _____ per game.'

Solution

(i) Expected value, $E(x) = \sum xP(x)$:

    1. Multiply the probability of obtaining each number $P(x)$ by the number x to get $xP(x)$.

    2. Sum all of the $xP(x)$ to find $E(x)$.

From the table, we find $E(x) = 2.9$.
This means that the average score expected is 2·9.

x	P(x)	xP(x)
1	0·25	0·25
2	0·25	0·50
3	0·15	0·45
4	0·15	0·60
5	0·1	0·50
6	0·1	0·60
$\sum xP(x) = 2.9$		

(ii) With a fair die, the probability of obtaining each number is one-sixth.

Expected value, $E(x) = \sum xP(x)$:

    1. Multiply the probability of obtaining each number $P(x)$ by the number x to get $xP(x)$.

    2. Sum all of the $xP(x)$ to find $E(x)$.

From the table, we find $E(x) = 3.5$. This means that the average value expected to roll is 3·5.

It cost €3 to play a game at the funfair. You win the number of euro shown on the die.

With the biased die you expect to win €2·90. However, given that you paid €3 to play the game, your net loss will be 10 cent, per game.

x	P(x)	xP(x)
1	$\frac{1}{6}$	$\frac{1}{6}$
2	$\frac{1}{6}$	$\frac{2}{6}$
3	$\frac{1}{6}$	$\frac{3}{6}$
4	$\frac{1}{6}$	$\frac{4}{6}$
5	$\frac{1}{6}$	$\frac{5}{6}$
6	$\frac{1}{6}$	1
$\sum xP(x) = \frac{21}{6} = 3.5$		

With the fair die you expect to win €3·50. However, given that you paid €3 to play the game, your net win will be 50 cent, per game.

So we can complete the sentence as follows:

'If you play the game many times with a fair die, you will win an average of 50c per game, but if you play with the biased die you will lose an average of 10c per game.'

key point

It is important for you to be aware that the expected value does not have to be one of the outcomes.

exam Q

(2017 Q.1)

According to the Central Statistics Office (CSO) there were 65,909 babies born in Ireland in 2015.

Of these, 32,290 were girls.

(a) (i) How many boys were born in Ireland in 2015?

    (ii) Find the probability that a baby picked at random from those born in Ireland in 2015 is a boy. Give your answer correct to two decimal places.

(b) Eight babies were born in Limerick's Maternity Hospital on 1 May 2015.

    (i) Use your answer to part (a)(ii) to find the probability that the first three babies born were boys. Give your answer correct to four decimal places.

    (ii) Find the probability that the third birth was the first girl born in the hospital that day. Give your answer correct to four decimal places.

(c) The table below shows the probability of being born on a particular day of the week.

    (i) Complete the table

Day	Mon	Tue	Wed	Thu	Fri	Sat	Sun
Probability	0·14		0·15	0·18	0·15	0·12	0·1

    (ii) In a particular week 1,300 babies were born.

    Find the number of babies expected to be born on the Tuesday of that week.

Solution

(a) (i) Number of boys = Total number − number of girls

    Number of boys = 65,909 − 32,290

    Number of boys = 33,619

    (ii) $P(\text{boy}) = \dfrac{\text{Number of boys}}{\text{Total number of babies}} = \dfrac{33{,}619}{65{,}909} = 0\cdot51$

(b) (i) $P(\text{3 boys}) = 0\cdot51 \times 0\cdot51 \times 0\cdot51 = 0\cdot1327$

    (ii) $P(\text{boy, boy, girl}) = 0\cdot51 \times 0\cdot51 \times 0\cdot49 = 0\cdot1274$

(c) (i) All probabilities sum to 1:

    $P(\text{Tuesday}) = 1 - (0\cdot14 + 0\cdot15 + 0\cdot18 + 0\cdot15 + 0\cdot12 + 0\cdot1)$

    $P(\text{Tuesday}) = 1 - 0\cdot84$

    $P(\text{Tuesday}) = 0\cdot16$

    Completed table:

Day	Mon	Tue	Wed	Thu	Fri	Sat	Sun
Probability	0·14	0·16	0·15	0·18	0·15	0·12	0·1

    (ii) Number born on a Tuesday = P(Tuesday) × Number of babies born

    Number born on a Tuesday = 0·16 × 1,300

    Number born on a Tuesday = 208

11 Statistics I: Statistical Investigations

aims

☐ To know the types of statistical data

☐ To be very familiar with the terms used in studying statistics, referring to the glossary of statistical terms at the back of this book

☐ To learn what is required when gathering and interpreting statistical data

Introduction to statistics

Statistics deals with the collection, presentation, analysis and interpretation of data. Insurance (of people and property), which now dominates many aspects of our lives, utilises statistical methodology. Social scientists, psychologists, pollsters, medical researchers, governments and many others use statistical methodology to study behaviours of populations.

Statistics deals with events which have more than one possible outcome. If you buy a sandwich in the school canteen priced at €2·20 and offer the cashier a €5 note, you should receive €2·80 in change. This is not statistics, as there is (or should be) only one amount of change possible.

If the school canteen manager wishes to know how much students spend when visiting the canteen, this is statistics because different customers spend different amounts.

The quantity which varies – in this case, the amount of money – is called a **variable**.

A collection of variables is referred to as **data** in statistics.

An **observation** is the value of a variable for one particular element of the sample or population, for example your sandwich purchase.

A **data set** is all the observations of a particular variable for the elements of the sample, for example a complete list of the canteen transactions of all students from your class on a certain day.

Types of data

Data are a collection of facts. It can be numbers, measurements, descriptions or observations. On our course we consider **two** types of data: quantitative and qualitative.

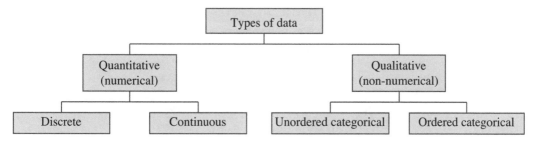

Quantitative data (numerical)

Discrete numerical data	Continuous numerical data
Discrete numerical data are data which can only have certain values.	Continuous data are data which can take any numerical value within a certain range.
Examples are number of students in a school, number of goals scored in a match and shoe sizes (including half-sizes).	Examples are time, weight, height, temperature, pressure and area. (Accuracy depends on the measuring device used.)

Qualitative data (non-numerical)

Unordered categorical data	Ordered categorical data
Unordered categorical data are data that can be counted but only described in words without any order or ranking.	Ordered categorical data are data that can be counted but only described in words and have an order or ranking.
Examples are colours, names, type of car and gender (male or female).	Examples are examination grades, football divisions and income groups.

Note: Ordered categorical data are sometimes called **ordinal data**.
If a code is used to put data into a category, the data is called **nominal data**. The data are assigned a code in the form of a number or letter. The numbers or letters are simply labels. For example, males could be coded as 1 and females as 2. Marital status can be coded as M if married or S if single. Nominal data can be counted but not measured or ordered.

Primary and secondary data

Primary data (first-hand data) are data that you collect yourself or are collected by someone under your direct supervision.

Secondary data (second-hand data) is data that have already been collected and made available from an external source such as newspapers, government departments, organisations or the internet.

Primary and secondary data have advantages and disadvantages.

Data	Advantages	Disadvantages
Primary	Know how it was obtained Accuracy is also known	Time consuming Can be expensive
Secondary	Easy and cheap to obtain	Could be out of date May have mistakes and be biased Unknown source of collection

Example

Classify each of the following variables in terms of data type: qualitative/quantitative, etc.

  (i) Colours of flowers
 (ii) Number of bicycles owned by students in your school
(iii) Ages of students in a primary school
 (iv) Volumes of contents of water bottles
  (v) Countries of birth of Irish citizens
 (vi) Number of strokes to complete a round of golf
(vii) Proportions of faulty fridges in samples of size fifty
(viii) Diameter of tennis balls
 (ix) Examination grades
  (x) Makes of TV in a salesroom

Solution

  (i) Qualitative – unordered categorical
 (ii) Quantitative – discrete numerical
(iii) Quantitative – continuous numerical   (but age in years is discrete)
 (iv) Quantitative – continuous numerical
  (v) Qualitative – unordered categorical
 (vi) Quantitative – discrete numerical
(vii) Quantitative – discrete numerical
(viii) Quantitative – continuous numerical
 (ix) Qualitative – ordered categorical (ordinal)
  (x) Qualitative – unordered categorical

Populations and samples

To find out the average weight of men in Ireland, we could, in theory, measure them all. In practice, this would be almost impossible. It would take too long and cost too much. Instead, we can measure the weights of a sample. Provided the sample is carefully chosen we can obtain almost as much information from the sample as from measuring the weight of every man in Ireland.

In statistics, we distinguish between a **population** and a **sample**.

> **key point**
>
> A **population** is all the possible data and a **sample** is part of the data.

The population is all the possible data

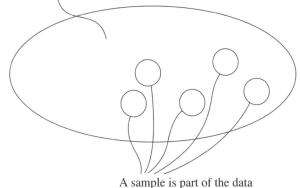

A sample is part of the data

Sampling is useful because it reduces the amount of data you need to collect and process. It also allows you to carry out a test without affecting all the population. For example, the contents of a sample of tubs of margarine, from a large batch, might be weighed to ensure that the actual contents matched that claimed on the label. Emptying the tubs to weigh the margarine makes them unsaleable, so it would be ridiculous to weigh the contents of the whole population of tubs.

> **key point**
>
>
>
> In conclusion, a sample is a small part of the population selected for surveying. A random sample is a sample in which every member of the population has an equal chance of being selected, and the selections are made independently.

exam Q

An Irish sports journalist intends to write a book about the English Football Premiership. She will analyse all Premiership matches in the season. For each match she records whether it is a home win, an away win or a draw. She also records, for each match, the total number of goals scored and the amount of time played before a goal is scored. Reference books showed that in the previous season, the mean number of goals per game was 2·345. On the first weekend of the season she recorded the number of goals scored in each match and calculated the mean number of goals per match as 2·6.

After carefully reading the above passage, identify an example of:

(i) A population   (v) A continuous variable

(ii) A sample   (vi) Primary data

(iii) A qualitative variable   (vii) Secondary data

(iv) A discrete variable

Solution

(i) Populations mentioned in the passage will relate to all Premiership matches played in the season and are either the results, the total number of goals or the amounts of time played before a goal is scored.

(ii) A sample would be the total number of goals scored in each match played, for example on the fourth weekend of the season.

(iii) A qualitative variable would be the result of matches Home Win (H), Away Win (A), Draw (D).

(iv) A discrete variable would be the number of goals scored in each match.

(v) A continuous variable would be the amount of time played before a goal is scored.

(vi) Primary data would be the data the journalist collected in that season.

(vii) Secondary data (obtained from a reference book) would be the mean number of goals per game in the previous season.

Sampling without bias

When you are selecting a sample, you need to avoid **bias** – anything which makes the sample unrepresentative. For example, if you want to estimate how often residents of Waterford visit the cinema in a year, it would be foolish to stand outside a cinema as the audience is coming out and ask people as they pass. This would give a biased sample, as all the people you ask would have been to the cinema at least once that year. You can avoid bias by taking a random sample.

Random sampling

Suppose the population consists of the heights of 100 students in a college and you wish to take a sample of size 5. The students' names are arranged in alphabetical order and numbered 00 to 99. A number between 00 and 19 is selected by lottery methods. For example, place 20 equally sized balls numbered 00 to 19 in a bag and ask a blindfolded assistant to pick one out. This student and every 20th one thereafter are chosen and their heights measured. That is, if the number 13 is selected, then the students numbered 13, 33, 53, 73 and 93 are chosen. Every student would have an equal chance of being chosen. However, a sister and brother who were next to each other in the alphabetical list could never both be included in the same sample, so this is **not** a random sample.

Usually, if you decide to choose five students at random you intend to choose five different students and would not consider choosing the same student twice. This is known as sampling without replacement.

key point

- For a sample to be random, every member of the population must have an equal chance of being selected.
- A random sample chosen without replacement is called a simple random sample.

exam Q

(2015 Q.9 (a))

The heights of a random 1,000 students were collected and recorded.

Tick one box from the table to indicate how you would categorise the type of data collected. Explain your choice.

Categorical Nominal	
Categorical Ordinal	
Numerical Discrete	
Numerical Continuous	

Solution

I chose Numerical Continuous because height is a number and can also take an infinity of values between any two consecutive numbers.

Categorical Nominal	
Categorical Ordinal	
Numerical Discrete	
Numerical Continuous	✓

exam Q

Jack goes to an all boys' school. He decides to carry out a survey to determine the amount of time students spend on the internet per week. Jack chose 30 students at random from his own school register and asked each of these students the time, to the nearest hour, they spend on the internet. The raw data were recorded as follows.

8	15	0	9	22	11	8	17	17	23
1	7	10	15	16	20	22	19	4	2
12	15	18	18	18	4	9	20	21	0

Complete the following grouped frequency table.

Time spent on the internet	0–4	5–9	10–14	15–19	20–24
Tally					
Number of students					

(i) Is this primary or secondary data? Give a reason for your answer.

(ii) Is the data discrete or continuous? Explain your answer.

(iii) Jack's friend Jim says, 'A larger sample will always give a better estimate of what we are trying to measure for the population, regardless of how it is chosen.' Do you agree with Jim? Justify your opinion.

(iv) Can you identify two possible sources of bias in Jacks survey?

(v) Suggest two ways Jack could improve his sample to make it more representative nationally.

Solution

Time spent on the internet	0–4	5–9	10–14	15–19	20–24
Tally	卌 I	卌	III	卌 卌	卌 I
Number of students	6	5	3	10	6

(i) This is primary data, as Jack collected the data himself.

(ii) Times are rounded to the nearest hour. This is discrete data.

(iii) Disagree with Jim because a larger sample which is not representative of the underlying population will not give a better estimate of what we are trying to measure for the population. It must first be a random sample, where every item in the population has an equal probability of being selected in the sample.

(iv) Some examples of sources of bias:
- Only boys in the survey ⇒ gender bias
- Only one school surveyed ⇒ may not be representative of the population as a whole
- Survey may not have been answered honestly, e.g. students may understate internet time if they are embarrassed to admit the actual time spent on the internet.

(v) Some examples of how to improve his sample:
- Include an all girls' school
- Include a coeducation school
- Include schools from outside the area
- Ask better questions to eliminate over/underestimates from students
- Take account of how different age groups affect the result.

12 Statistics II: Central Tendency and Spread of Data

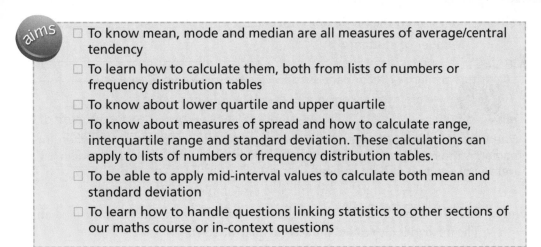

aims

- [ ] To know mean, mode and median are all measures of average/central tendency
- [ ] To learn how to calculate them, both from lists of numbers or frequency distribution tables
- [ ] To know about lower quartile and upper quartile
- [ ] To know about measures of spread and how to calculate range, interquartile range and standard deviation. These calculations can apply to lists of numbers or frequency distribution tables.
- [ ] To be able to apply mid-interval values to calculate both mean and standard deviation
- [ ] To learn how to handle questions linking statistics to other sections of our maths course or in-context questions

Averages

There are many types of averages. Three that we meet initially are called the mean, the mode and the median. They are also known as measures of central tendency.

Mean

The mean is the proper name for what most people call the average.

key point

The mean of a set of values is defined as the sum of all the values divided by the number of values.

That is:

$$\text{Mean} = \frac{\text{Sum of all the values}}{\text{Number of values}}$$

The formula is often written as: $\mu = \dfrac{\Sigma x}{n}$ (see *booklet of formulae and tables*, page 33)

Note: Σ, pronounced sigma, means the sum of (i.e. Σx means 'add up all the x-values').

μ, pronounced mew, is the symbol for the mean.

Mode

The mode of a set of items is the item that occurs most often. If there are no repeated items, then the mode does not exist.

Median

When the values are arranged in ascending or descending order of size, then the median is the middle value. If the number of values is even, then the median is the average of the two middle values.

Note: Half the values lie below the median and half the values lie above the median. The median is also called the second quartile (Q_2).

Example

The ages of the seven dwarfs are as follows.

Name	Happy	Doc	Sleepy	Sneezy	Dopey	Grumpy	Bashful
Age	685	702	498	539	402	685	619

(i) Find the mean age.

(ii) Find the (mode) modal age.

(iii) Find the median age.

Solution

(i) Mean age $= \dfrac{\text{Sum of all their ages}}{\text{Number of dwarfs}} = \dfrac{\Sigma x}{n}$

$\text{Mean} = \dfrac{685 + 702 + 498 + 539 + 402 + 685 + 619}{7}$

$\mu = \text{Mean} = \dfrac{4{,}130}{7} = 590$

(ii) Mode $= 685$ The number that occurs most often

(Happy and Grumpy are twins!)

(iii) Median $=$ middle value in ascending or descending order

$= 702, 685, 685, \mathbf{619}, 539, 498, 402$

$= 619$

The mean and the median need not necessarily be members of the original set of values, while the mode, if it exists, is always a member of the original set of values.

A note on averages

Average	Advantages	Disadvantages
Mean	• Useful for further analysis • Uses all the data • Easy to calculate	• Distorted by extreme results • Mean is not always a given data value
Mode	• Easy to find • Not influenced by extreme values • Is the only measure suitable for qualitative nominal data	• Not very useful for further analysis • May not exist
Median	• Useful for further analysis • Unaffected by extremes • Easy to calculate if data are ordered	• Not always a given data value • Can be difficult to calculate

Example

Write down a set of five positive integers with:

(i) Mean of 8

(ii) Mean of 8 and mode of 3

(iii) Mean of 8, mode of 3 and median of 9

(iv) Mean of 8, mode of 3, median of 9 and range of 10

(Range = Highest value − Lowest value)

Solution

To have a mean of 8 the five numbers must sum to 40.

(i) {5, 6, 7, 8, 14} or {1, 2, 3, 4, 30} or lots of other choices

(ii) {3, 3, 3, 14, 17} or {3, 3, 7, 10, 17} or {1, 2, 3, 3, 31} or lots of other choices

(iii) {3, 3, 9, 10, 15} less choices here

(iv) {3, 3, 9, 12, 13} only one choice here

Example

A survey of a housing estate with 36 houses is undertaken by a city council. The survey recorded the number of occupants per house as follows:

0	7	5	5	6	6	2	4	5	6	7	4
4	6	5	6	5	5	4	3	2	7	6	5
0	6	5	6	6	6	4	6	6	5	4	2

(i) Represent the information in a frequency distribution table.

(ii) Calculate the mean number of occupants per house.

(iii) What is the mode?

(iv) Suggest a reason why two houses recorded no occupants.

(v) What insights can you draw from your answers to (i) to (iv) as to the number of people, age distribution and social conditions in the estate?

Solution

(i) Frequency distribution table

Number of occupants per house	0	1	2	3	4	5	6	7
Number of houses	2	0	3	1	6	9	12	3

(ii) For a frequency distribution

$$\text{Mean} = \mu = \frac{\Sigma fx}{\Sigma f} \quad \text{(from \textit{booklet of formulae and tables}, page 33)}$$

$$= \frac{(2)(0) + (0)(1) + (3)(2) + (1)(3) + (6)(4) + (9)(5) + (12)(6) + (3)(7)}{2 + 0 + 3 + 1 + 6 + 9 + 12 + 3}$$

$$= \frac{0 + 0 + 6 + 3 + 24 + 45 + 72 + 21}{36} = \frac{171}{36} = 4{\cdot}75$$

Or you can use your calculator.

(iii) Mode = most common number = 6, which is recorded 12 times.

(iv) Two houses recorded no occupants because:

- The houses were unoccupied for some reason (fire, vandalism, holidays)
- The surveyors were not answered when they called
- The houses were for sale.

(v) 171 people with a mean house occupancy of almost five (4·75) could indicate large young families (or extended families). Two unoccupied houses might indicate a somewhat derelict neighbourhood if boarded up.

27 students in a class each recorded the amount, €x, they spent in the school shop during the Monday morning break. The total amount spent was €57·24.

(i) Find the mean amount spent per student during the Monday morning break.

(ii) One extra student joined the class and reported she spent €5·20 during the Monday morning break. Calculate the new mean including the extra student.

Solution

(i) Mean = $\dfrac{\text{Total amount spent}}{\text{Total number of students}} = \dfrac{57{\cdot}24}{27} = €2{\cdot}12$

(ii) Total for 28 students = €57·24 + €5·20 = €62·44

∴ New mean = $\dfrac{62{\cdot}44}{28} = €2{\cdot}23$

The first five terms of an arithmetic sequence are e, f, 17, g, h. Calculate the mean of these five numbers. Justify your answer.

Solution

For an arithmetic sequence, we can write:

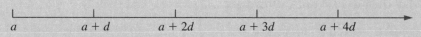

The mean of five numbers is given by $\dfrac{\Sigma x}{5}$.

$$\text{Mean} = \frac{a + (a + d) + (a + 2d) + (a + 3d) + (a + 4d)}{5}$$

$$\text{Mean} = \frac{5a + 10d}{5}$$

$$\text{Mean} = a + 2d = \text{the middle term}$$

The middle term in e, f, 17, g, h is 17 and they are in an arithmetic sequence.

∴ Mean = the middle term = $a + 2d = 17$.

The above work is my justification.

Alternatively, in any arithmetic sequence with an odd number of terms, the mean is always the middle term.

Three measures of spread

1. The range

The range is the difference between the highest data value and the lowest data value.

Range = highest value − lowest value

2. The interquartile range

Quartiles, as their name suggests, are the quarter-way divisions of the data.

The **lower quartile**, Q_1, is the value one-quarter of the way through the distribution.

The **upper quartile**, Q_3, is the value three-quarters of the way through the distribution. Q_1 and Q_3 are found in a similar way to the median, except we start off at one-quarter and three-quarters, respectively, of the total.

Here is a diagram to help clarify the situation.

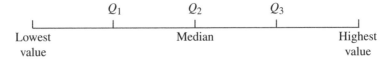

$$Q_1 \qquad\qquad Q_2 \qquad\qquad Q_3$$

Lowest value   Median   Highest value

The **interquartile range** = upper quartile value − lower quartile value = $Q_3 - Q_1$. Therefore, half the values in a distribution must lie between the upper and lower quartile. The interquartile range is a number.

The interquartile range gives a measure of the spread of the values about the median.

The median is often referred to as Q_2.

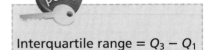

> **key point**
>
> Interquartile range = $Q_3 - Q_1$

exam Q

A box contains 50 cards. Each card has a number from 1 to 6 written on it. The following table shows the frequencies for each number.

(i) Calculate the value of k.

(ii) Find **(a)** the median

   (b) the interquartile range.

Number	1	2	3	4	5	6
Frequency	13	5	10	k	13	7

Solution

(i) $13 + 5 + 10 + k + 13 + 7 = 50$

$$48 + k = 50$$

$$k = 2$$

(ii) Using a line plot:

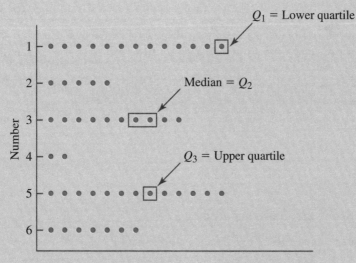

Q_1 = Lower quartile

Median = Q_2

Q_3 = Upper quartile

(a) Median (= Q_2) is associated with the middle value = $\dfrac{3 + 3}{2}$ = 3.

(b) Interquartile range = upper quartile − lower quartile

$$= Q_3 - Q_1$$
$$= 5 - 1$$
$$= 4$$

3. Standard deviation

Standard deviation gives us an indication of how the values are spread out. The higher the standard deviation, the more spread out around the mean the data is, and vice versa. The Greek letter σ (lower case), sigma, is used to denote the standard deviation.

key point

Σ is capital sigma, σ is lower case sigma.

To calculate the standard deviation, σ, of a set of values, we use the following formula:

$$\sigma = \sqrt{\frac{\Sigma(x - \mu)^2}{n}}$$

(see *booklet of formulae and tables*, page 33)

where x represents the values
μ represents the mean
n is the number of values of x.

key point

Standard deviation, σ, is a measure of the spread from the mean of all values in the set.

The syllabus only requires you to correctly enter the data into a calculator and find σ.

If calculating σ by hand, it is good practice to lay out the data in vertical columns in a table.

Properties of the standard deviation

- σ measures the spread about the mean and should be used only when the mean is chosen as the measure of centre.
- $\sigma = 0$ only when there is *no spread*. This happens only when all observations have the same value. Otherwise, $\sigma > 0$. As the observations become more spread out about their mean, σ gets larger. We can say the higher the standard deviation, the greater the variability in the data.
- σ, like the mean, μ, is affected by extreme values.
- The square root in the formula for

$$\sigma = \sqrt{\frac{\Sigma(x - \mu)^2}{n}}$$

ensures that the x-values and the standard deviation are in the same units.
- You can use your calculator to calculate the standard deviation, σ. Calculator instructions can be found at the end of this book.

In summary, it is important to know that we have three ways of measuring the variability or spread of a distribution:

- The range
- The interquartile range
- The standard deviation, σ.

Example

Find the mean and standard deviation of the following sets of numbers.

(i) 4, 4, 4, 4, 4

(ii) 1, 3, $3\frac{1}{2}$, 4·2, 8·3

(iii) −196, −49, 25, 66, 174

(iv) Hence, interpret what your answers imply.

Solution

Using a calculator:

(i) $\mu = 4$ and $\sigma = 0$ $\Rightarrow$ data not spread out at all

(ii) $\mu = 4$ and $\sigma = 2\cdot4$

(iii) $\mu = 4$ and $\sigma = 123$

(iv) Interpretation

Each set has a mean = 4, and while set (i) has data that is not spread out at all, set (iii) has a much higher standard deviation than set (ii), confirming that set (iii) is much more spread out about the mean than set (ii).

Example

Calculate the standard deviation, correct to one decimal place, of the following array of numbers: 2, 4, 7, 8, 9.

Solution

First calculate the mean, μ.

Notice $n = 5$.

$$\mu = \frac{2 + 4 + 7 + 8 + 9}{5}$$

$$\mu = \frac{30}{5} = 6$$

Now make out a table:

x	$(x - \mu)$	$(x - \mu)^2$
2	2 − 6	16
4	4 − 6	4
7	7 − 6	1
8	8 − 6	4
9	9 − 6	9

$$\Sigma(x - \mu)^2 = 16 + 4 + 1 + 4 + 9 = 34$$

$$\text{Standard deviation} = \sigma = \sqrt{\frac{\Sigma(x - \mu)^2}{n}} = \sqrt{\frac{34}{5}} = 2\cdot607680962$$

$$\therefore \quad \sigma = 2\cdot6$$

Alternatively, you can choose to enter the data on a calculator to find $\sigma = 2\cdot6$.

The standard deviation of a frequency distribution

Standard deviation $= \sigma = \sqrt{\dfrac{\Sigma f(x - \mu)^2}{\Sigma f}}$ (see *booklet of formulae and tables*, page 33)

A test consisted of seven questions. One mark was awarded per question for a correct solution and no marks for an incorrect solution. The following distribution table shows how a class of students scored in the test.

Mark	0	1	2	3	4	5	6	7
No. of students	1	7	6	5	2	6	3	0

(i) Given the mean $\mu = 3$, calculate the standard deviation, σ, correct to two decimal places.

(ii) Five new students joined the class. The new students took the same test and achieved marks of 0, 1, 1, 3 and 7.

In each of the following questions, insert the correct letter in the box provided.

When the results of the five students were included with the original results:

(a) The mean mark for the class was:
  X – unchanged Y – decreased Z – increased   Answer ☐

(b) The standard deviation for the class was:
  X – unchanged Y – decreased Z – increased   Answer ☐

Justify your answer in each case.

Solution

(i) Enter the data on your calculator to find the standard deviation $\sigma = 1\cdot79$ correct to two decimal places. You do not need to know the mean is 3 when finding σ on a calculator. However, if you calculate σ by hand, i.e. setting up a table, then having the mean is useful.

(ii) (a) Answer $\boxed{Y}$ because the mean mark of
  the five new students $= \dfrac{0 + 1 + 1 + 3 + 7}{5} = \dfrac{12}{5} = 2\cdot4$.

  Since $2\cdot4 < 3$, the original mean, we conclude that the addition of five new students decreased the mean.

(b) Answer $\boxed{Z}$ because one of the new students achieved a score of seven.

  This new student increased the range from $6 - 0 = 6$ to $7 - 0 = 7$, thus the results were more spread out, which means the standard deviation was increased.

Grouped frequency distribution

We can estimate the mean and the standard deviation of a grouped frequency distribution by taking the mid-interval values of each class. Otherwise, the procedure is the same as before.

Example

The frequency distribution below shows the number of hours per week spent watching television by 37 people.

Hours	0–2	2–6	6–12	12–20	20–30
No. of people	5	9	12	6	5

(**Note:** 0–2 means 0 is included but 2 is not, and so on.)

Calculate: (i) The mean

(ii) The standard deviation of hours spent per week watching television.

Solution

(i) We assume the data to be at mid-interval values.

It is good practice to rewrite the table using these mid-interval values.

New table:

Hours (mid-interval values)	1	4	9	16	25
No. of people	5	9	12	6	5

$$\text{Mean} = \mu = \frac{\Sigma fx}{\Sigma f} = \frac{5(1) + 9(4) + 12(9) + 6(16) + 5(25)}{5 + 9 + 12 + 6 + 5}$$

$$= \frac{370}{37} = 10$$

∴ The mean number of hours spent watching television per week is 10 hours.

(ii) Continue by hand to calculate σ or using your calculator $\Rightarrow \sigma = 7\cdot5$.

(2015 Q.9 (b))

The heights of a random sample of 1,000 students were collected and recorded.

The sample of 1,000 students was made up of 500 boys and 500 girls. The data from the 500 girls was used to create the information shown in Table 1.

Table 1 (Girls)							
Height (cm)	145–150	150–155	155–160	160–165	165–170	170–175	175–180	180–185
Number of girls	15	48	80	112	125	81	29	10

(i) Use the information in Table 1 to estimate the mean height of the girls, using mid-interval values.

(ii) What is the largest possible value for the range of the heights of the girls in this sample?

(iii) The median height of the girls in the sample is 164·5 cm. Explain what this means in the context of the heights of the 500 girls.

Solution

(i) $\dfrac{(15)(147·5) + (48)(152·5) + (80)(157·5) + (112)(162·5) + (125)(167·5) + (81)(172·5) + (29)(177·5) + (10)(182·5)}{15 + 48 + 80 + 112 + 125 + 81 + 29 + 10}$

$= \dfrac{82215}{500} = 164·43$ cm

(ii) Largest possible range $= 185 - 145 = 40$ cm

(iii) 250 girls are 164·5 cm tall or taller and 250 girls are 164·5 cm tall or shorter

This question was worth a total of 30 marks.

(i) 20 marks **(ii)** 5 marks **(iii)** 5 marks

In part **(i)**, 10 marks were awarded for any work of merit. Unusually, full credit (20 marks) was awarded for the correct answer without work in this part.

(SEC sample)

The size, mean and standard deviation of four sets of data, A, B, C and D, are given in this table:

	A	B	C	D
Size (n)	12	50	50	500
Mean (μ)	15	15	55	5
Standard deviation	4	4	8	10

Complete the sentences below by inserting the relevant letter in each space.

(i) On average, the data in set _____ are the biggest numbers and the data in set _____ are the smallest numbers.

(ii) The set that contains more numbers than any other is _____ and the set that contains fewer numbers than any other is _____.

(iii) The set with the greatest total is _____.

(iv) The data in set _____ are more spread out than the data in the other sets.

(v) The set that *must* contain some negative numbers is set _____.

Solution

(i) On average, the data in set ___C___ are the biggest numbers and the data in set ___D___ are the smallest numbers.

Notice: C has a mean = 55 which is by far the biggest.

(ii) The set that contains more numbers than any other is ___D___ and the set that contains fewer numbers than any other is ___A___.

Notice: D has 500 numbers, A has only 12 numbers

(iii) A has total = 12 × 15 = 180

B has total = 50 × 15 = 750

C has total = 50 × 55 = 2,750

D has total = 500 × 5 = 2,500

∴ The set with the greatest total is ___C___

(iv) The data in set ___D___ are more spread out than the data in the other sets.

This is because D has the greatest standard deviation ⟹ more spread out.

(v) The set that *must* contain some negative numbers is set ___D___.

Because since $\mu = 5$ and $\sigma = 10$ the numbers are spread out in the following way:

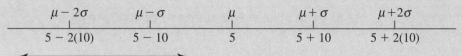

Conclude set D *must* have some negative numbers.

13 Statistics III: Representing and Analysing Data

aims

☐ To know how to construct and answer questions on bar charts, histograms, pie charts, stem and leaf diagrams, and scatter plots

☐ To understand the idea of correlation and how to decide on the strength of a given correlation

☐ To be clear on the difference between correlation and causality

☐ To cope with exam questions incorporating statistical information and displays

Pie charts and bar charts

exam Q

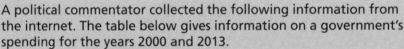

A political commentator collected the following information from the internet. The table below gives information on a government's spending for the years 2000 and 2013.

Numbers for 2013 are given in billions and numbers for 2000 are given in millions.

Category of spending	Year 2013 € billion	Year 2013 % of total spending	Year 2000 € million
Defence	1·0		730
Education	9·3		4,090
Health	14·6		5,700
Social security and welfare	22·0		7,800
Agriculture, forestry and fishing	2·6		1,400
Public debt	8·7		6,010
Other spending	23·9		9,290
Total government expenditure	82·1 billion		35,020 million

The commentator also constructed the pie chart (shown opposite) on government spending for the year 2013.

Government Spending 2013

- Defence 1%
- Education
- Other spending 29%
- Health 18%
- Social security and welfare 27%
- Public debt 11%
- Agriculture, forestry and fishing 3%

(i) Write down the total government expenditure for 2013 and 2000 in euro (instead of billions of euro and millions of euro).

(ii) Write the total amount spent for 2000 in billions.

(iii) How much, in billions, did total government expenditure increase by from 2000 to 2013?

(iv) Calculate the percentage increase in government expenditure from 2000 to 2013.

(v) What percentage (to the nearest whole number) of the budget was spent on education in 2013? Use the table and/or the pie chart.

(vi) What percentage (to the nearest whole number) of the budget was spent on education in 2000? How does this compare with the percentage spent on education in 2013?

(vii) Aside from other spending, in 2013 which categories received the most and least government spending?

(viii) Draw a bar chart of government spending for 2013 using 'Percentage spent in each category' on the y-axis.

(ix) Do you think one of the charts (pie or bar) is better than the other at communicating the information in the table? Explain your answer.

(x) Explain how to calculate the size of the angle to represent government spending on health in the given pie chart for 2013.

Solution

(i)

key point

1 billion = 1,000 million

i.e. 1,000,000,000 = 1,000 × 1,000,000

Spending for 2013 = €82·1 billion

= €82,100,000,000

Spending for 2000 = €35,020 million

= €35,020,000,000

(ii) €35,020 million = €35·02 billion   (divide by 1,000)

(iii)   €82·1   billion spent in 2013
−€35·02   billion spent in 2000
€47·08   billion increase

(iv) Percentage increase = $\dfrac{\text{Actual increase}}{\text{Total amount spent in 2000}} \times 100\% = \dfrac{47 \cdot 08}{35 \cdot 02} \times 100\%$

$= 134 \cdot 4\%$

(v) Pie chart:

% spent on education = 100% − (1% + 29% + 11% + 3% + 27% + 18%)

= 100% − 89% = 11%

(vi) Year 2000 from given table:

$\dfrac{\text{Amount spent on education}}{\text{Total amount spent}} \times 100\% = \dfrac{4{,}090}{35{,}020} \times 100\% = 12\%$

When education spending in 2000 (12%) is compared to education spending in 2013 (11%), a decrease of 1% is recorded. However, the actual amount spent on education was hugely increased in that period.

(vii) In 2013, defence was the lowest government spending category while social security + welfare was the highest government spending category.

(viii)   Government spending 2013

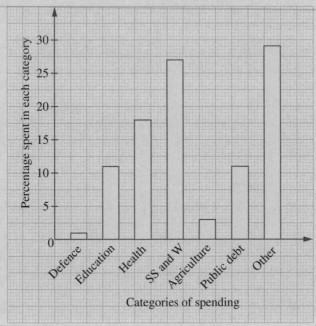

(ix) The bar chart makes it much easier to distinguish differences when they are fairly close and to clearly order individual categories, both with each other and in the group as a whole.

However, the pie chart shows how all the categories, relate to the total spending.

(x) From the given table, health spending = €9·3 billion in 2013.

$$\% \text{ spending on health} = \frac{9\cdot3 \times 100\%}{82\cdot1} = 11\%$$

For a pie chart 100% = 360°

$$1\% = \frac{360}{100}$$

$$11\% = \frac{360 \times 11}{100} = 40°$$

Histograms

A histogram is often used to display information contained in a frequency distribution. The essential characteristic of a histogram is that the area of each rectangle represents the frequency, and the sum of the areas of the rectangles is equal to the sum of the frequencies.

Example

The histogram below shows the time spent by a group of women in a boutique.

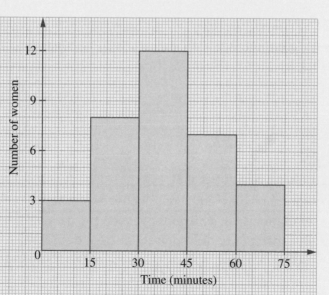

(i) Complete the following table.

Time (minutes)	0–15	15–30	30–45	45–60	60–75
Number of women					

(**Note:** 0–15 means 0 or more but less than 15, etc.)

(ii) How many women are in the group?

(iii) What is the least possible number of women who spent more than 50 minutes in the boutique?

(iv) The sentences below describe the type of data shown in the histogram above. Delete the incorrect word in each pair of brackets.

'This is a set of [univariate/bivariate] data. The data are [discrete/continuous].'

Solution

(i)

Time (minutes)	0–15	15–30	30–45	45–60	60–75
Number of women	3	8	12	7	4

(ii) $3 + 8 + 12 + 7 + 4 = 34$ women in the group

(iii) The seven women in the class interval 45–60 minutes could all have spent less than 50 minutes in the boutique.

∴ Least possible number of women who spent more than 50 minutes in the boutique is four, i.e. all those in the class interval 60–70 minutes.

(iv) This is a set of **univariate** data, i.e. only one variable (in this case, time). The data are **continuous**, e.g. 15 minutes and 43 seconds; 58·99 minutes; $20\frac{1}{9}$ minutes, etc.

exam focus

It is useful to remember that:

- Bar charts have equal gaps between the bars.
- Histograms have no gaps between the bars.
- Bar charts can only represent discrete data.
- Histograms can represent discrete or continuous data.

(2017 Q.9 (a), (b))

In June 2016, the UK held a referendum on its membership of the EU. Table 1 below summarises the results.

Table 1	
United Kingdom EU Membership Referendum 2016	
	Votes
Leave the EU	17,410,742
Remain a member of the EU	16,141,241
Valid votes	33,551,983
Invalid or blank votes	
Total votes	33,577,342

Source: The UK Electoral Commission

(a) (i) Write the number of *invalid or blank votes* into the table.

(ii) Write the number who voted to *leave the EU* as a percentage of the *valid* votes. Give your answer correct to the nearest percent.

(b) Table 2 shows the percentages of 'Remain' and 'Leave' voters in various age groups of those who voted in the referendum.

Table 2		
	Remain (%)	**Leave (%)**
18–24	73	27
25–34	62	38
35–44	52	48
45–54	44	56
55–64	43	57
65+	40	60

(i) Draw a suitable chart or charts to represent the data in Table 2.

(ii) Find the mean of the 'Remain' values given in Table 2 **and** find the mean of the 'Leave' values given in Table 2. Give your answers as percentages, correct to two decimal places.

(iii) Explain why the answers to part **(b) (ii)** do not accurately reflect the actual outcome of the referendum.

Solution

(a) (i) 33,577,342 − 33,551,983 = 25,359 invalid or blank votes

(ii) $\dfrac{17,410,742}{33,551,983} \times \dfrac{100}{1} = 51 \cdot 891\% = 52\%$

(b) (i)

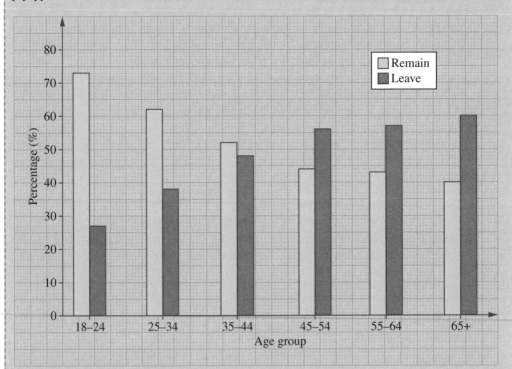

(ii)

Total remain = 73 + 62 + 52 + 44 + 43 + 40 = 314%

$\dfrac{\text{Total \%}}{6 \text{ categories}} = \dfrac{314}{6} = 52 \cdot 33\%$

Total leave = 27 + 38 + 48 + 56 + 57 + 60 = 286%

$\dfrac{\text{Total \%}}{6 \text{ categories}} = \dfrac{286}{6} = 47 \cdot 67\%$

The above calculations imply the remain vote prevailed (won)!

(iii) The results from **(b) (ii)** do not accurately reflect the actual outcome of the referendum because the number of voters in each age group are not equal.

Distributions and shapes of histograms

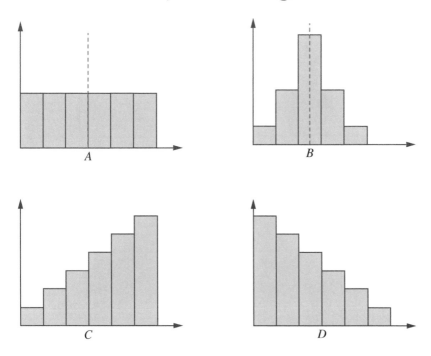

Histograms come in many different shapes. Above we have four histograms, all with different shapes:

 A has **uniform distribution** and is **symmetric** (balanced).

 B has a **symmetric** shape (later you will see that this is a **normal** distribution).

 C has **no axis of symmetry**. It is **negatively skewed**, that is, there is a tail at the negative end of the distribution.

 D has **no axis of symmetry** and is **positively skewed**.

A swimming club run a triathlon race for charity. The race consists of a 750 m swim, followed by a 20 km cycle followed by a 5 km run.

76 athletes completed this triathlon.

An analysis of the race data, using statistical software, produces the following histograms of the times for the three events.

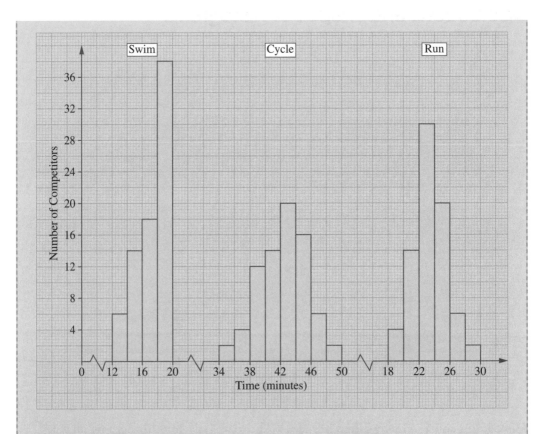

(i) Use the histograms to complete the following sentences.

   (a) The event that, on average, takes longest to complete is the _____.

   (b) In all three histograms, the times are grouped into intervals of _____ minutes.

   (c) The time of the fastest person in the swim was between _____ and _____ minutes.

   (d) The event in which the times are most spread out is the _____.

(ii) Use the terms 'symmetric' or 'positively skewed' or 'negatively skewed' to describe the distribution of competitors for:

   (a) The swim   **(b)** The cycle   **(c)** The run.

(iii) Give an estimate for the average time taken by a competitor to complete the triathlon. Justify your answer.

Solution

(i) Use the histograms to complete the following sentences.

(a) The event that, on average, takes longest to complete is the ___cycle___.

(b) In all three histograms, the times are grouped into intervals of ___2___ minutes.

(c) The time of the fastest person in the swim was between ___12___ and ___14___ minutes.

(d) The event in which the times are most spread out is the ___cycle___.

(ii) The distribution of competitors for

(a) The swim is negatively skewed

(b) The cycle is symmetric

(c) The run is symmetric

(iii) 'Reading' the following answers from the histogram:

The average swimmer takes 18 minutes to finish.

The average cyclist takes 43 minutes to finish.

The average runner takes 23 minutes to finish.

∴ Estimate for the total average time taken to complete the triathlon
= 18 + 43 + 23 = 84 minutes.

Alternatively, using the mid interval values with the frequencies, we calculate
μ = 17·3, 42·4 and 23·4 respectively
⟹ Total average time = 17·3 + 42·4 + 23·4 = 83·1 minutes.

Stem and leaf diagrams

A stem and leaf diagram is a useful way of presenting data. It shows all the original data and gives the overall picture or shape of the distribution.

It is similar to a horizontal histogram, with the numbers themselves forming the rectangles.

Stem and leaf diagrams are suitable only for small amounts of data.

The ages of a group of 12 people are given as:

6   8   12   15   17   23   23   28   30   32   37   44

This can be represented on a stem and leaf diagram as shown below.

0	6 8
1	2 5 7
2	3 3 ⑧
3	0 2 7
4	4

This represents 28: stem = 2, leaf = 8.

Key: 1 | 7 = 17

You must always add a key to show how the stem and leaf combine.

Example

(i) Use a back-to-back stem and leaf diagram to compare the results of a survey for a group of 18 boys and 18 girls. Each boy and girl was asked to write down the number of good friends they had.

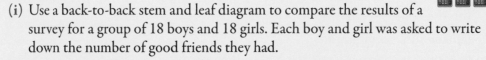

Number of good friends for girls	18	6	19	28	26	22	15	28	31	15	36	25	22	31	18	5	16	13
Number of good friends for boys	7	23	0	22	4	12	15	18	13	12	3	14	21	0	27	6	23	21

(ii) Find from your stem and leaf diagram Q_3, the upper quartile (or 75th percentile), for:
   (a) Girls   (b) Boys.

(iii) Describe the shape of the distributions for:
   (a) Girls   (b) Boys.

(iv) Emer drew the stem and leaf diagram because she thought that these two groups would be about the same. Do you think that the diagram would cause Emer to confirm her belief or change it? Give reasons for your answer.

Solution

(i) The plot before rearranging (unordered):

Key: Boys
5 | 1 = 15

Key: Girls
1 | 5 = 15

Boys		Girls
6 0 3 4 0 7	0	6 5
4 2 3 8 5 2	1	8 9 5 5 8 6 3
1 3 7 1 2 3	2	8 6 2 8 5 2
	3	1 6 1

key point

Notice the left-hand side key is reversed.

The final plot arranged in order:

Key: Boys
$1\,|\,2 = 21$

Key: Girls
$2\,|\,5 = 25$

Boys		Girls
7 6 4 3 0 0	0	5 6
8 5 4 3 2 2	1	3 5 5 6 8 8 9
7 3 3 2 1 1	2	2 2 5 6 8 8
	3	1 1 6

If the exam does not provide enough space to construct two diagrams, as above, it is good exam technique to ask for extra paper and construct your diagrams on that.

(ii) (a) The upper quartile (or 75th percentile) for girls is the 14th highest score on the diagram for girls. Hence, the upper quartile $= Q_3 = 28$.

(b) The upper quartile (or 75th percentile) for boys is the 14th highest score on the diagram for boys. Hence, the upper quartile $= Q_3 = 21$.

(iii) The shape of the distribution for:

(a) Girls is symmetric

(b) Boys is uniform and symmetric.

(iv) While the shapes of the distributions for each group are very different, it is the significantly higher Q_3 score for the girls (seven friends more than the boys) that would cause Emer to change her belief.

Always be sure to work with an **ordered** stem and leaf diagram.

An educator believes that new Maths methods will help Leaving Certificate students improve their Maths grades. She arranges for a Leaving Cert class of 21 students to take part in new Maths methods for a one-year period.

A control class of 24 Leaving Cert students follows the traditional Maths methods. At the end of the year a Maths test is given to all students. The results in percentages are given on the ordered back-to-back stem and leaf plots.

4	3	1 9
5 4	4	2 2
8 7 6 2	5	1 3 7 9 9 9
8 6 6 3 3 1	6	0 6 2 8
7 6 3 2 2	7	1 1 3 5
8 5 4	8	1 2 8

Write down four errors in the above ordered back-to-back stem and leaf plot.

Solution

Error 1: The plot does not indicate which group is traditional and which is new Maths.

Error 2: The right-hand side line is not ordered.

$$6 \mid 0\ 6\ 2\ 8$$

It should read:

$$6 \mid 0\ 2\ 6\ 8$$

Error 3: There are 21 readings on both sides of the plot. One side should have 24 readings.

Error 4: No key on either side.

    e.g.   Right-hand side $7 \mid 3 = 73\%$

             Left-hand side $6 \mid 5 = 56\%$

(2016 Q.5)

The waiting times, in minutes, for 16 patients at a dentist's surgery are recorded for a particular week (**Week 1**) on the following stem and leaf plot.

Week 2		Week 1
	0	5 8
	1	2 2 2 3
	2	0 4 5 7
	3	0 1 2 4 4
	4	4

Key = 1 | 3 = 13 minutes

(a) Find the mode and the median of the data.

(b) Find the mean waiting time for **Week 1**, correct to one decimal place.

(c) The waiting times were recorded again the following week. The results were:

27, 23, 6, 15, 18, 29, 16, 17, 15, 18, 40, 32, 16, 12, 28, 9

Solution

(a) Mode = most common = 12

Median = middle = $\dfrac{24 + 25}{2}$ = 24·5

(b) Mean = $\dfrac{\text{Total minutes}}{\text{Number of patients}}$ = $\dfrac{363}{16}$ = 22·7

(c)

Week 2		Week 1
9 6	0	5 8
8 8 7 6 6 5 5 2	1	2 2 2 3
9 8 7 3	2	0 4 5 7
2	3	0 1 2 4 4
0	4	4

Key = 3 | 2 = 23 minutes   Key = 1 | 3 = 13 minutes

Correlation

Scatter plots (graphs)

Is the number of cigarettes smoked by an individual related to the age of their death?

Are your overall Leaving Certificate results related to the number of hours you spend at your part-time job?

key point

Scatter plots are used whenever we are examining possible relationships between two variables (bivariate data).

To look at the relationship between two sets of quantitative data, we plot the points on a graph (similar to x-axis/y-axis). Data that come in pairs are called **bivariate data**.

Scatter plot patterns

Here are three scatter diagrams that are typical of what we meet.

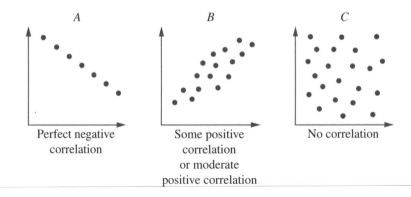

A	B	C
Perfect negative correlation	Some positive correlation or moderate positive correlation	No correlation

We get negative correlation where increasing values of one variable are associated with generally decreasing values of the other variable (case *A* on the previous page).

We get positive correlation where increasing values of one variable are associated with generally increasing values of the other variable (case *B* on the previous page).

We have no correlation when the points are randomly and widely spaced out (case *C* on the previous page).

Note: Correlation measures the strength of the linear association between two quantitative variables. Before using correlation, check the following.

1. Are both variables quantitative?
2. Check the scatter plot for evidence of 'straightness', i.e. can you visualise a straight line passing through the plot and representing the relationship?
3. Check for outliers and extreme values (stragglers). Outliers are very important and always deserve special attention. Outliers can make a weak correlation look strong or can hide a strong correlation.

The Type Fast secretarial training agency has a new computer software spreadsheet package. The agency investigates the number of hours it takes people of varying ages to reach a level of proficiency using this package. Fifteen individuals are tested and the results are summarised in the table below.

Age (x)	32	40	21	45	24	19	17	21	27	54	33	37	23	45	18
Time (in hours) (y)	10	12	8	15	7	8	6	9	11	16	t	13	9	17	5

(i) Given the mean time taken was 10·6 hours, calculate the value of *t*.

(ii) Plot the data on a scatter plot.

(iii) Comment on the strength and direction of the correlation of the scatter plot in **(ii)**.

(iv) Give two possible problems that might make the results of the investigation unreliable. State clearly why the issue you mention could cause a problem.

Solution

(i) This is an equation in disguise.

$$\frac{10 + 12 + 8 + 15 + 7 + 8 + 6 + 9 + 11 + 16 + t + 13 + 9 + 17 + 5}{15} = 10\cdot6$$

$$\frac{146 + t}{15} = 10\cdot6$$

$$146 + t = 159 \qquad \text{multiply both sides by 15)}$$

$$t = 13 \qquad \text{(subtract 146 from both sides)}$$

(ii)

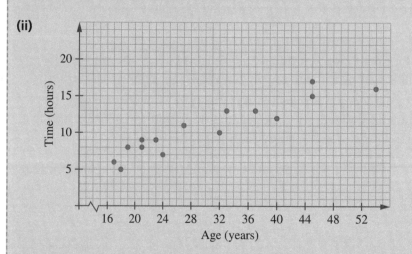

(iii) The correlation is moderate to strong and it is in the positive direction. It indicates that older people take longer to reach a level of proficiency.

(iv) One possible problem would be if the individuals were not chosen at random.

A second possible problem could be caused by gender imbalance, i.e. are women more proficient than men at this task?

A third (not asked for) possible problem could be the restricted age range of those investigated. The question considers ages from 17–45 plus one 54 year old. Perhaps an age range of 16–60 years would be better.

It is good practice in the exam if asked to supply two reasons or problems in the question, as in **(iv)** above, to provide one extra suggestion if you can. However, do not write an essay. Remember, you are taking a Maths exam.

At the same time, it is important to note that if you are asked to select *one* answer from a given list or tick *one* box in a multiple choice question, then you select/tick one and only one.

The correlation coefficient, r

Measuring correlation of scatter plots (scatter graphs)

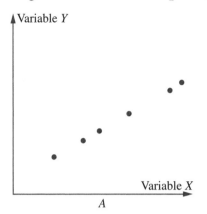

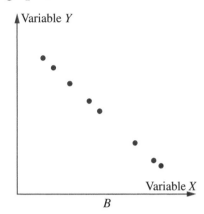

The points on scatter graph *A* are in a straight line. In this case we say there is **perfect positive correlation** between the two variables, *X* and *Y*.

We use the letter *r* to represent the correlation. We say that $r = 1$ when we have perfect positive correlation.

The points on scatter graph *B* are in a straight line. In this case we say there is **perfect negative correlation** between the two variables, *X* and *Y*.

We say that $r = -1$ when we have perfect negative correlation.

How the correlation, *r*, measures the direction and strength of a linear association:

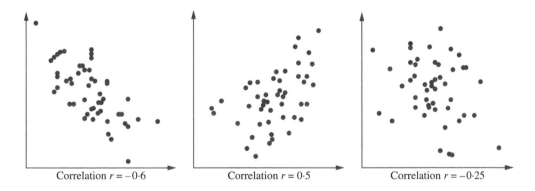

Correlation $r = -0.6$ Correlation $r = 0.5$ Correlation $r = -0.25$

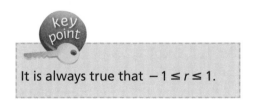

key point

It is always true that $-1 \le r \le 1$.

Example

Snow White and the seven dwarfs have their heights and weights measured.
On the scatter plot, Snow White is represented by W.

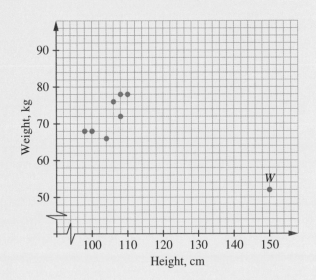

(i) From the plot, write down the bivariate data (couple) for Snow White.

(ii) The correlation coefficient between height and weight for the seven dwarfs
is one of the numbers below. State clearly the letter corresponding to the
correct answer.

(A) 0·9   (B) −0·4   (C) 0·2   (D) 2·1   (E) −0·8

(iii) The correlation coefficient between height and weight for Snow White and the
seven dwarfs is one of the numbers below. State clearly the letter corresponding to
the correct answer.

(P) −1·4   (Q) 0·8   (R) 1·1   (S) 0·7   (T) −0·7

(iv) Sleepy has the lowest weight. How many dwarfs are taller than Sleepy?

(v) One of the eight data points is an outlier. Which one? Justify your selection.

Solution

(i) Bivariate data for Snow White = (150, 52).

(ii) Strong positive correlation ⇒ (A).   (The taller dwarfs are heavier)

(iii) Moderate negative correlation ⇒ (T).

(iv) Four dwarfs are taller than Sleepy, i.e. every dwarf to the right of Sleepy
(104, 66) on the scatter plot.

(v) Snow White (150, 52) does not fit on the scatter plot with the rest of the
points. W is clearly the outlier.

key point

An outlier is a value in a distribution that is noticeably more extreme than the majority of values. Whether a value is an outlier or not is decided by (you) the researcher.

exam Q

Statements *A, B, C, D* and *E* represent descriptions of the correlation between two variables:

A High positive linear correlation

B Low positive linear correlation

C No correlation

D Low negative linear correlation

E High negative linear correlation

Which statement best represents the relationship between the two variables shown in each of the scatter diagrams below?

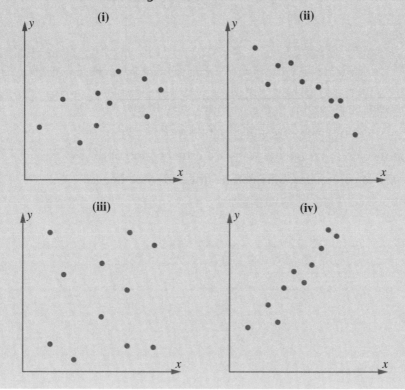

Solution

Vital to stress positive or negative.

(i) positive   **(ii)** negative

(iii) ??   **(iv)** positive

Therefore

(i) *B*   **(ii)** *E*   **(iii)** *C*   **(iv)** *A*

key point

The phrase 'moderate correlation' is not used in this question. We sometimes use the words strong for high and weak for low when describing correlation.

exam Q

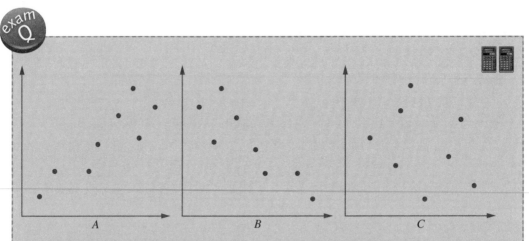

Match the scatter diagrams *A*, *B*, *C* with the statements *P*, *Q*, *R*.

P As you get older, your eyesight disimproves.

Q Students who are good at maths are usually good at physics.

R There is no connection between height and intelligence.

Solution

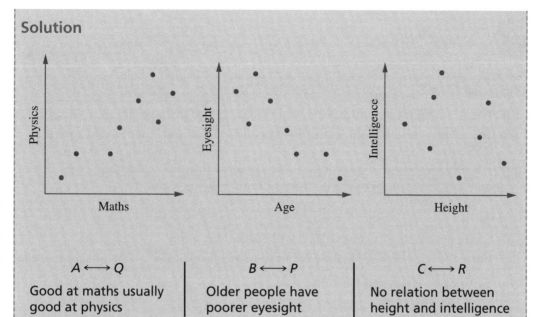

$$A \longleftrightarrow Q$$

Good at maths usually good at physics

$$B \longleftrightarrow P$$

Older people have poorer eyesight

$$C \longleftrightarrow R$$

No relation between height and intelligence

In statistics we often refer to the x-axis as the independent variable and the y-axis as the dependent variable. The following table illustrates the previous situations.

x-axis independent variable	y-axis dependent variable
Maths	Physics
Age	Eyesight
Height	Intelligence

Each of the following statements contains a blunder. Explain in each case what is wrong.

(i) There is a high correlation between the gender of Irish workers and income.

(ii) The correlation between planting rate and yield of potatoes was found to be 0·55 tons.

(iii) A high correlation was found ($r = 2·03$) between students' ratings of their teachers and ratings made by the students' parents.

Solution

(i) Gender is categorical data. Correlation does not apply.

Note: Correlation applies only when two sets of quantative data are compared.

(ii) Correlation is never a quantity.

$r = 0·55$ is OK   but $r = 0·55$ **tons** is not correct.

(iii) $-1 \leq r \leq 1$: r is never above 1

r is never below -1

Explain, with the aid of an example, what is meant by the statement: 'Correlation does not imply causality.'

Solution

Attracta said, 'We had a fire in our house recently. Five firemen and one fire engine were called to deal with it. The insurance company paid the claim of €17,000 for the damage.'

Her friend Noreen replied, 'We had a fire in our house last year. Eighteen firemen and two fire engines were called to deal with it. The insurance company paid the claim of €235,000 for the damage. Those firemen caused a frightful mess.'

Correlation between two variables does not automatically mean that one causes the other, e.g. as the number of firemen fighting the fire rises, so does the insurance claim. The size, strength, duration and ferocity of the fire increases the size of the claim, not the firemen. However, the number of firemen present is related to the dimensions of the fire.

Alternatively in a primary school there might be a correlation between reading ability and shoe size, but big feet don't make you read better and reading doesn't make your feet grow! In this case, both variables are connected to age – a 'confounding factor'.

Recap on correlation and its coefficient, r:

- Correlation is a measure of the extent of the linear relationship between two variables.
- When using words to describe correlation, we must first decide whether it is positive or negative, then decide if it is weak, moderate or strong.
- r is positive when there is a positive association between the variables, e.g. between the age of a car and the total distance it has travelled.
- r is negative when there is a negative association between the variables, e.g. between the age of a car and the price of a car.
- Using a number to describe correlation, we write the number r, where r is a value from -1 to $+1$.
- r is never a value above 1.
- r is never a value below -1.
- It is important that you are able to match a given correlation coefficient with a given scatter plot.
- It is vital to understand that correlation does not imply causality.

14 Statistics IV: The Normal Curve and the Empirical Rule

aims

☐ To know about and to apply the Empirical Rule for the normal curve
☐ To apply your knowledge of the normal distribution to examination questions

Introduction to the normal curve

The normal distribution

Many continuous variables, which occur naturally, have a shape like this:

This is called a normal distribution. It has a high probability density close to the mean and this decreases as you move away from the mean.

Examples of variables that are likely to follow a normal distribution are:

(i) The lengths of leaves from oak trees

(ii) The times taken by 10-year-old girls to run 100 m

(iii) The heights of adult males in Ireland

(iv) The widths of car doors coming off a production line.

key point

The main features of normal distribution are that it is:

• Bell shaped
• Symmetrical (about the mean)
• The total area under the curve is 1 = 100%
• Mean = Mode = Median

The standard deviation, σ, controls the spread about the mean, μ, of a normal distribution. The smaller the standard deviation, the more concentrated the data and the larger the standard deviation, the more spread out the data.

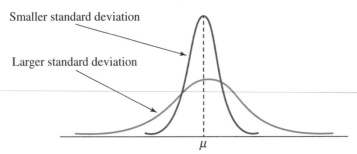

Smaller standard deviation

Larger standard deviation

μ

Empirical Rule

key point

Empirical Rule (68%, 95% or 99·7%) for the normal distribution

For many large populations, the Empirical Rule provides an estimate of the approximate percentage of observations that are contained within one, two or three standard deviations of the mean.

- Approximately 68% of the observations are in the interval $\mu \pm 1\sigma$.
- Approximately 95% of the observations are in the interval $\mu \pm 2\sigma$.
- Approximately 99·7% of the observations are in the interval $\mu \pm 3\sigma$.

This can be represented by the following graph:

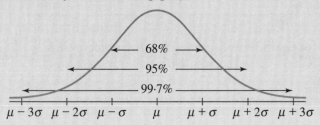

Example

Consider the CAO points required to gain entry to a third-level college course. Suppose the mean number of CAO points is 320, with a standard deviation of 80, then:

- $\mu \pm 1\sigma = 320 \pm 80$ covers 68% of candidates
- $\mu \pm 2\sigma = 320 \pm 160$ covers 95% of candidates
- $\mu \pm 3\sigma = 320 \pm 240$ covers 99·7% of candidates.

(i) Represent the situation on a normal distribution curve.

(ii) Use the Empirical Rule to complete the following sentence: 95% of all CAO candidates score between _____ and _____ points.

(iii) Use the Empirical Rule to make one other statement about the CAO points of candidates.

Solution

(i)

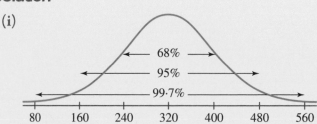

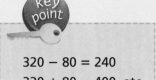

key point

320 − 80 = 240
320 + 80 = 400, etc.

(ii) 95% of all CAO candidates score between 160 and 480 points.
(iii) 68% of all CAO candidates score between 240 and 400 points.

exam focus

It is vital for candidates to remember the percentages (68%, 95%, 99·7%) associated with the Empirical Rule.

exam Q

(2017 Q.5)

In a survey, the IQ scores of 1,200 people were recorded. The mean score was 100 points and the standard deviation was 15 points. Assuming that IQ scores are normally distributed, the data are shown on the diagram below.

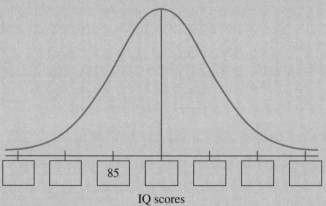

IQ scores

(i) Fill in the missing numbers on the horizontal axis.

(ii) A person is chosen at random from those surveyed. Use the Empirical Rule to find the probability that this person has an IQ score between 70 and 130 points.

(iii) Use the Empirical Rule to find the approximate number of people surveyed with an IQ score of between 85 and 115 points.

Solution

(i)

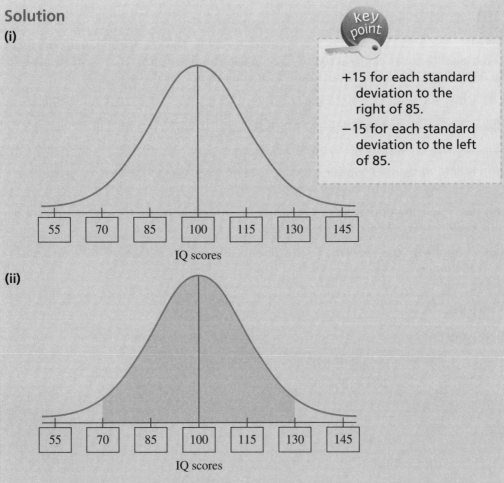

(ii)

From the Empirical Rule, 95% of people scored between ± 2 standard deviations. The probability this person has an IQ score between 70 and 130 points is 95% = 0·95.

(iii)

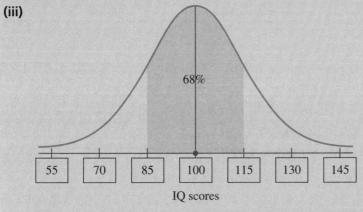

From the Empirical Rule, 68% of people scored between 61 standard deviations. Finally, calculate 68% of the 1200 people surveyed to get:

$$\frac{1200}{100} \times 68 = 816 \text{ people}$$

A national test was constructed to have marks ranging from 100 to 250 and to be normally distributed for the range.

 (i) What is the mean mark on this test?

 (ii) What is the median mark on this test?

(iii) What is the modal mark on this test?

(iv) If 84% of students obtained marks of less than 196 on the test, estimate the standard deviation of marks for this test.

 (v) What are the end points of the interval which has its centre at the mean and within which 95% of the marks lie?

(vi) Write down the percentage of students who scored between 133 marks and 154 marks.

Solution

(i) (ii) and (iii)

Because the normal distribution is symmetric, then:

$$\text{Mean} = \mu = \frac{100 + 250}{2} = 175$$

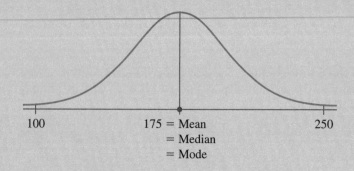

$$
\begin{array}{ccc}
100 & 175 = \text{Mean} & 250 \\
 & = \text{Median} & \\
 & = \text{Mode} &
\end{array}
$$

key point

For the normal distribution:
Mean = Median = Mode

(iv) The Empirical Rule may be used to subdivide the normal curve distribution (using symmetric property) into the following sections:

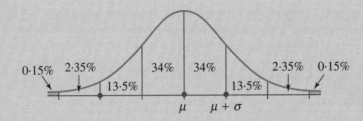

 key point

- 0·15% + 2·35% + 13·5% + 34% + 34% = 84% from the above graph ⟹ 84% of students score $< \mu + \sigma$.
- The Empirical Rule ignores the two tails of the normal curve (shaded above) which represents 100% − 99·7% = 0·3% of the population. That is, 0·3% ÷ 2 = 0·15% on each tail.

Finally, we state $\mu + \sigma = 196$

$$175 + \sigma = 196$$

$$\sigma = 21 \quad \text{(subtract 175 from both sides)}$$

(v)

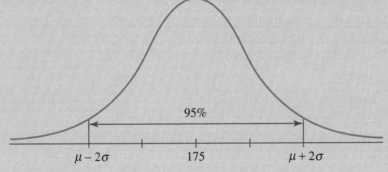

The Empirical Rule tells us that 95% of the data are found between $\mu - 2\sigma$ and $\mu + 2\sigma$.

Hence, the end points of the interval are given by 175 − 2(21) and 175 + 2(21).

= [175 − 42, 175 + 42]

= [133, 217]

(vi)

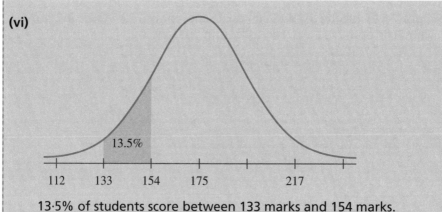

13·5% of students score between 133 marks and 154 marks.

Example

The table below shows the ages of 40 golfers in a competition.

34	52	39	50	56	45	31	66	60	53
53	28	52	29	47	39	40	41	28	48
62	49	49	37	37	48	48	47	19	38
48	58	38	43	38	23	48	58	35	26

(i) Calculate, correct to one decimal place, the mean and standard deviation of the data.

(ii) Show that the Empirical Rule holds true for
  (a) One standard deviation around the mean
  (b) Two standard deviations around the mean.

Solution

(i) Using your calculator

Mean = $\bar{x}$ = 43·5 and standard deviation = σ = 11.

(ii) (a) Upper range = mean + one standard deviation
$$= 43·5 + 11$$
$$= 54·5$$
Lower range = mean − one standard deviation
$$= 43·5 - 11$$
$$= 32·5.$$
Of the forty golfers, 27 (count them yourself!) are aged between 32·5 and
54·5 years that is $\dfrac{27}{40} \times 100 = 67·5\%$

Hence, approximately 68% of the golfers are aged between 32·5 and 54·5 years.

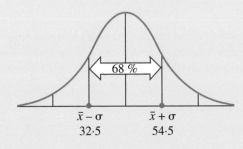

(b) Upper range = mean + two standard deviations
$$= 43·5 + 2(11)$$
$$= 65·5$$
    Lower range = mean − two standard deviations
$$= 43·5 − 2(11)$$
$$= 21·5$$

Of the forty golfers, 38 (count them yourself!) are aged between 21·5 and 65·5 that is $\dfrac{38}{40} \times 100 = 95\%$

Hence approximately 95% of the golfers are aged between 21·5 and 65·5 years.

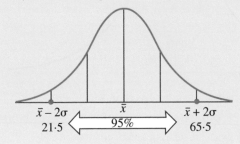

Assume that the duration of human pregnancies is normally distributed. The length of time each pregnancy lasts varies slightly. At least 95% of pregnancies last between 236 days and 300 days.

  (i) What is the greatest standard deviation which can be allowed to achieve this?
 (ii) What is the mean length of each pregnancy?
(iii) What percentage of pregnancies last longer than one standard deviation above the mean?
 (iv) For every 4,000 births, approximately how many will have lasted more than 284 days?
  (v) The duration of human pregnancies may not actually follow a normal distribution as described above. Explain why it may be somewhat skewed to the left.

Solution

  (i)

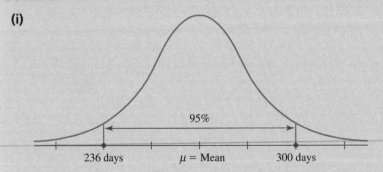

Empirical Rule $\Rightarrow$ From 236 days to 300 days is four standard deviations

$$\Rightarrow 300 - 236 = 4\sigma$$
$$64 = 4\sigma$$
$$16 = \sigma$$

Hence, the greatest standard deviation which achieves this is 16 days.

 (ii) From the graph in (i), we observe μ is midway between 236 days and 300 days because the normal distribution is symmetric in shape.

$$\Rightarrow \mu = \frac{236 + 300}{2} = \frac{536}{2} = 268 \text{ days}$$

(iii)

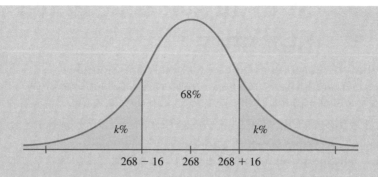

From the graph:

$$k\% + 68\% + k\% = 100\%$$
$$2k\% = 32\%$$
$$k\% = 16\%$$

This tells us that 16% of all pregnancies last longer than one standard deviation above the mean.

(iv) 16% of every 4,000 births will have lasted more than 284 days.

$$100\% = 4{,}000$$
$$1\% = \frac{4{,}000}{100}$$
$$16\% = \frac{4{,}000 \times 16}{100} = 640 \text{ births}$$

(v) There are not as many very long pregnancies nowadays due to births being induced after a certain stage.

Hence, the curve is skewed to the left (negatively skewed).

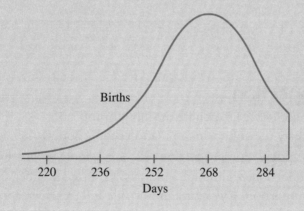

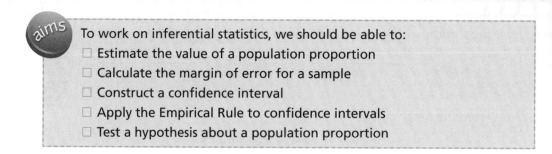

15 Statistics V: Inferential Statistics

aims

To work on inferential statistics, we should be able to:
- ☐ Estimate the value of a population proportion
- ☐ Calculate the margin of error for a sample
- ☐ Construct a confidence interval
- ☐ Apply the Empirical Rule to confidence intervals
- ☐ Test a hypothesis about a population proportion

Inferential statistics is the branch of statistics that uses probability and statistics to draw conclusions from data that are affected by random variation.

Introduction to confidence intervals

When results of surveys are reported in the media, they often include a statement like: **39% of respondents favour the government in the upcoming election. However, there is a margin of error of 3%.**

What this means is the people who carried out the survey are reasonably confident that in the real election, the percentage of votes for the government will be 39% ± 3%.

In other words, they are confident that if the election was held now, the government would receive somewhere between 36% and 42% of the vote.

We may show this confidence interval as:

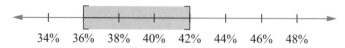

34%   36%   38%   40%   42%   44%   46%   48%

Sample proportion

We use $\hat{p}$ (pronounced 'p hat') to denote the sample proportion. $\hat{p}$ is the statistic that will be used to estimate the unknown population proportion, p.

$$p = \text{population proportion} \qquad \hat{p} = \text{sample proportion}$$

The population proportion, p, although unknown, is a fixed number. On the other hand, the sample proportion, $\hat{p}$, is a random variable and its value depends on chance. Suppose we wanted to know the proportion (percentage) of people in Ireland who are left-handed. We randomly selected 400 people and found that 64 of them are left-handed.

$$\hat{p} = \frac{\text{Number of people in the sample who are left-handed}}{\text{Number of people sampled}} = \frac{64}{400} = 0 \cdot 16 \ (16\%)$$

If 72 out of 400 people sampled were left-handed, then:

$$\hat{p} = \frac{72}{400} = 0\cdot18\ (18\%)$$

Notice that the value of $\hat{p}$, the sample proportion, changes depending on the sample chosen. If the sample chosen is a good representation of the population, then $\hat{p}$, the sample proportion, will be a good estimate of the true population proportion, p.

Example

Write down the sample proportion, $\hat{p}$, in each of the following.

(i) In a market research survey, 187 people out of a random sample of 561 from a certain area said that they used a particular brand of toothpaste.

(ii) A survey was carried out on 7,410 randomly selected people and the result was that 6,175 were in favour of holding an election now.

(iii) An insurance company conducted a survey of 845 car crashes. It found that 338 of the crashes occurred within 6 km of the driver's home.

Solution

Remember:

$$\hat{p} = \frac{\text{The number of 'successes' in the sample}}{\text{The sample size}}$$

(i) $\hat{p} = \dfrac{187}{561} = \dfrac{1}{3}$

(ii) $\hat{p} = \dfrac{6,175}{7,410} = \dfrac{5}{6}$

(iii) $\hat{p} = \dfrac{338}{845} = \dfrac{2}{5}$

Margin of error

We now look at the real business of statistics: to save people time and money! None of us want to do unnecessary work and statistics can tell us exactly how lazy we can afford to be. Our problem is that the collections of things in the world are so large, it's very difficult to get the information we want, e.g. voting populations, what percentage favours each candidate, what is the average length of sardines to fit in a can, what proportion of TVs will be defective.

We could answer questions like this by measuring every sardine in the world and doing some calculations. This method is not for statisticians: they want the easy way out.

Statisticians take **samples**. A sample is a relatively small subset of the total population, e.g. pollsters at election time.

An obvious question is: How big a sample do we have to take to get a meaningful result?

The answer turns out to involve $\dfrac{1}{\sqrt{n}}$, where n is the number of items in the sample.

In statistics, the margin of error is a number that represents the accuracy of a survey. An estimate from a survey should be treated with caution.

The margin of error is denoted by E. The margin of error, at the 95% level of confidence, is given by:

Margin of error $= E = \dfrac{1}{\sqrt{n}}$

where n is the size of the sample.

If $n = 100$: $\quad E = \dfrac{1}{\sqrt{100}} = 0\cdot1 = 10\%$

If $n = 400$: $\quad E = \dfrac{1}{\sqrt{400}} = 0\cdot05 = 5\%$

If $n = 1{,}000$: $\quad E = \dfrac{1}{\sqrt{1{,}000}} = 0\cdot0316227766 = 3\cdot16\%$ $\quad$ (correct to two decimal places)

If $n = 10{,}000$: $\quad E = \dfrac{1}{\sqrt{10{,}000}} = 0\cdot01 = 1\%$

Some notes on margin of error

- On our course, the margin of error is **always** at the 95% level of confidence.
- As the sample size increases the margin of error decreases.
- At the 95% level of confidence a sample of about
  - **(i)** 80 has a margin of error approximately $\pm11\%$
  - **(ii)** 1,000 has a margin of error approximately $\pm3\cdot2\%$.
- The size of the (original) population does not matter.
- If the sample size, n, is doubled (say 500 to 1,000) the margin of error, E, is **not** halved.
- The margin of error estimates how accurately the results of a poll reflect the 'true' feelings of the population.

Example

Calculate the margin of error at the 95% level of confidence when the sample size is:

  (i) 25   (ii) 1,600   (iii) 2,000

Solution

Margin of error $= E = \dfrac{1}{\sqrt{n}}$

  (i) If $n = 25$ then $E = \dfrac{1}{\sqrt{25}} = \dfrac{1}{5} = 0{\cdot}2 = 20\%$

  (ii) If $n = 1{,}600$ then $E = \dfrac{1}{\sqrt{1{,}600}} = \dfrac{1}{40} = 0{\cdot}025 = 2{\cdot}5\%$

  (iii) If $n = 2{,}000$ then $E = \dfrac{1}{\sqrt{2{,}000}} = 0{\cdot}0223606 = 2{\cdot}24\%$ (correct to two decimal places)

Example

At the 95% confidence level, calculate the sample size, n, to have a margin of error of:

  (i) 1·25%   (ii) 2·5%

Solution

Margin of error $= E = \dfrac{1}{\sqrt{n}}$

(i) $1{\cdot}25\% = 0{\cdot}0125$

    $\dfrac{1}{\sqrt{n}} = 0{\cdot}0125$

      $1 = 0{\cdot}0125\sqrt{n}$

    (multiply both sides by $\sqrt{n}$)

    $\dfrac{1}{0{\cdot}0125} = \sqrt{n}$

    (divide both sides by 0·0125)

(ii) $2{\cdot}5\% = 0{\cdot}025$

    $\dfrac{1}{\sqrt{n}} = 0{\cdot}025$

      $1 = 0{\cdot}025\sqrt{n}$

    (multiply both sides by $\sqrt{n}$)

    $\dfrac{1}{0{\cdot}025} = \sqrt{n}$

    (divide both sides by 0·025)

$$\left(\frac{1}{0\cdot0125}\right)^2 = n$$

(square both sides)

$$6{,}400 = n$$

$$\left(\frac{1}{0\cdot025}\right)^2 = n$$

(square both sides)

$$1{,}600 = n$$

key point

Notice in this example when we double the margin of error (from 1·25% to 2·5%) the sample size is **not** halved (from 6,400 to 1,600).

95% confidence interval

The estimated proportion plus or minus its margin of error is called a confidence interval for the true proportion. The 95% confidence for a proportion is given by:

key point

Sample proportion − margin of error ≤ true proportion ≤ sample proportion + margin of error

$$\hat{p} - \frac{1}{\sqrt{n}} \le p \le \hat{p} + \frac{1}{\sqrt{n}}$$

where n is the sample size, p is the population proportion and $\hat{p}$ is the sample proportion.

We can state with 95% confidence that the true population, p, lies inside this interval. What this means is that if the same population was surveyed on numerous occasions and the confidence interval was calculated, then about 95% of these confidence intervals would contain the true proportion and about 5% of these confidence intervals would not contain the true proportion.

The end points of the 95% confidence are given by $\hat{p} \pm \dfrac{1}{\sqrt{n}}$.

The 95% confidence interval

$\hat{p} - \dfrac{1}{\sqrt{n}}$ $\hat{p} + \dfrac{1}{\sqrt{n}}$

What does '95% confidence' really mean?

What do we mean when we say we have 95% confidence that our interval contains the randomly selected value? Formally, what we mean is that '95% of randomly selected values will fall into the confidence interval'. This is correct but somewhat long-winded, so we usually say 'we are 95% confident that the (randomly) selected value lies in our interval'.

Our uncertainty is about whether the particular (randomly) selected value is one of the successful ones or one of the 5% that falls outside the interval.

Example

Show on separate diagrams the following confidence intervals.

(i) $0.2 \leq p \leq 0.45$

(ii) In a clinical study, 68% of patients reported relief after taking a new drug. The margin of error was calculated as 4%.

Solution

(i) $0.2 \leq p \leq 0.45$

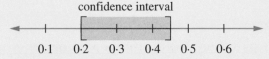

(ii) $68\% - 4\% \leq p \leq 68\% + 4\%$

$$64\% \leq p \leq 72\%$$

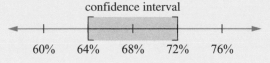

Example

Noah is sitting his Leaving Cert in June. After Christmas he made an estimate of how many CAO points he expected to get.

His estimate was 405 CAO points. Noah was not very confident of his estimate so he allowed each of his six subject grades go up or down by 11 points. Construct a confidence interval for Noah's CAO points estimate.

Solution

6 subjects by 11 points each = 6 × 11 = 66 points

Noah's lowest estimate would be 405 − 66 = 339

Noah's highest estimate would be 405 + 66 = 471

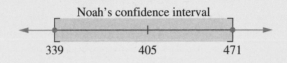

Noah's confidence interval

339   405   471

(2015 Q.6 (b))

A few days before the Scottish Independence Referendum in September 2014, a *YouGov* poll estimated the support for the 'No' campaign to be 54%.

(i) If *YouGov* sampled 1,000 people, find the margin of error.
Write your answer as a percentage, correct to one decimal place.

(ii) Create a 95% confidence interval for the level of support for the 'No' campaign in the population.

The standard of answering on this question was disastrous. A question similar to this will **definitely** appear in the future.

Solution

(i) Margin of error $= E = \dfrac{1}{\sqrt{n}} = \dfrac{1}{\sqrt{1000}} = 0.0316 = 3.2\%$

(ii)

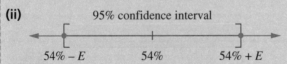

95% confidence interval

$54\% - E$ 54% $54\% + E$

To calculate the end points of the confidence interval:

$54\% - E = 54\% - 3.2\% = 50.8\%$

$54\% + E = 54\% + 3.2\% = 57.2\%$

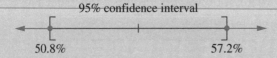

95% confidence interval

50.8%   57.2%

Hypothesis testing

A hypothesis is a statement (or theory) whose truth has yet to be proven or disproven. Examples of hypotheses:

- More than half the population is satisfied with EU membership
- Drinking fizzy drinks causes tooth decay
- The age of marriage has increased over the past 20 years.

The null hypothesis:

The statement being tested in a test of significance is called the **null hypothesis**. The test of significance is designed to assess the strength of the evidence against the null hypothesis. Usually the null hypothesis is a statement of no effect or no difference. We abbreviate 'null hypothesis' as H_0.

Statistics help to make decisions

We can use statistics to reject or fail to reject claims.

1. Is global temperature increasing?
   The null hypothesis, H_0, is that global temperature is not increasing, i.e. there is no difference in temperature. The alternative hypothesis, H_A, is that global temperature is increasing.
2. Is a new drug effective at treating HIV/AIDS?
   The null hypothesis, H_0, is that the new drug is not effective. The alternative hypothesis, H_A, is that the new drug is effective.
3. Is a survey on left-handed people biased if it indicates that 24% of people are left-handed? The null hypothesis, H_0, is that 24% of people are left-handed, i.e. the survey is not biased. The alternative hypothesis, H_A, is that the survey is biased.

Often the people investigating the data hope to reject H_0. They hope:

(i) their new drug is better than the old one

or

(ii) the new ad campaign is better than the original

or

(iii) the new machine is better than the existing one.

However, in statistics, it is essential that our attitude is one of skepticism. Until we are convinced otherwise, we accept H_0. In other words, we cling to the idea that there is no change, no improvement, no deterioration, no effect.

The reasoning behind hypothesis testing is that we usually prefer to think about getting things right rather than getting them wrong. A similar logic applies in trials by jury, where the defendant is considered innocent until it is shown otherwise.

In a courtroom, the null hypothesis is that the defendant did **not** commit a crime. A verdict of guilty means we reject the hypothesis, that is to say, the defendant committed a crime. However, a verdict of not guilty does not mean the defendant did not commit a crime, but simply that the case has not been proven.

Procedure for carrying out a hypothesis test

The procedure for carrying out a hypothesis test will involve the following steps:

1. Write down H_0, the null hypothesis, and H_A, the alternative hypothesis.

For example, to test if a coin is biased if we get 6 heads in 10 tosses, we could formulate the following hypothesis:

H_0: The coin is not biased

H_A: The coin is biased.

2. Write down or calculate the sample proportion, $\hat{p}$.

3. Find the margin of error.

4. Write down the confidence interval for p, using

$$\hat{p} - \frac{1}{\sqrt{n}} \leq p \leq \hat{p} + \frac{1}{\sqrt{n}}.$$

In addition, we may illustrate the confidence interval with a diagram.

5. (i) If the value of the population proportion stated is within the confidence interval, we do not challenge H_0.

(ii) If the value of the population proportion is outside the confidence interval, reject the null hypothesis, H_0, and accept H_A.

(2017 Q.9 (c))

In the days following the UK referendum on Brexit, a survey was conducted in Ireland on attitudes towards a British exit from the European Union.

(i) 1,200 people were surveyed. Find the margin of error of this survey. Write your answer as a percentage. Give your answer correct to the nearest percent.

(ii) In the Irish survey, 578 of the 1,200 surveyed agreed that a UK exit would have a negative effect on the Irish economy. Use your answer to part **(i)** above to create a 95% confidence interval for the proportion of the Irish population who agreed that a UK exit would have a negative effect on the Irish economy.

(iii) After the survey, a political party claimed that 53% of the Irish population believed that the decision of the UK to leave the EU would have a negative effect on the Irish economy. Use your answer to part **(ii)** above to conduct a hypothesis test, at the 5% level of significance, to test the party's claim. Give your conclusion in the context of the question.

Solution

(i) Margin of error $= E = \dfrac{1}{\sqrt{n}} = \dfrac{1}{\sqrt{1200}} = 0{\cdot}02886 = 3\%$

(ii) $\hat{p} = \dfrac{578}{1200} = 0{\cdot}4816666 \to 48\%$

To calculate the end points of the confidence interval:

$48\% - E = 48\% - 3\% = 45\%$

$48\% + E = 48\% + 3\% = 51\%$

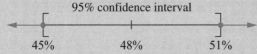
95% confidence interval
45%   48%   51%

(iii) $H_0: p = 53\%$

$H_A: p \neq 53\%$

Since the political party claim of 53% is outside the confidence interval we found in part **(ii)**, we reject the claim of the political party. Their claim is false.

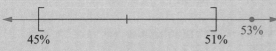
45%   51%   53%

Or reject H_0 because party claim is false.

Or at the 95% level of confidence (5% level of significance), the party's claim is not correct.

exam focus

Confidence intervals and hypothesis tests are not well known or understood.

The above question was very poorly answered by the majority of candidates.

FlyinAir airlines provides flights in Europe. Each month the company carries out a survey among 1,100 randomly selected passengers. The company repeatedly advertises that 75% of their customers are satisfied with their overall service. 803 of the sample stated they were satisfied with the overall service.

 (i) State the null hypothesis and the alternative hypothesis.

 (ii) Investigate at the 5% level of significance if the company was correct in saying that 75% of their customers were satisfied.

(iii) Clearly state your conclusion.

Solution

 (i) Null hypothesis: The proportion of passengers who are satisfied with the service is unchanged at 75%

or $H_0 : p = 0.75$.

Alternative hypothesis: The proportion of passengers who are satisfied with the service is changed, no longer 75%

or $H_A: p \neq 0.75$.

 (ii) Sample proportion = $\hat{p} = \dfrac{803}{1,100} = 0.73 = 73\%$

Margin of error = $E = \dfrac{1}{\sqrt{n}} = \dfrac{1}{\sqrt{1,100}} = 0.03015 = 3\%$

(iii) Confidence interval

$$\hat{p} - \frac{1}{\sqrt{n}} \leq p \leq \hat{p} + \frac{1}{\sqrt{n}}$$

$$73\% - 3\% \leq p \leq 73\% + 3\%$$

$$70\% \leq p \leq 76\%$$

95% confidence interval

68%   70%   73%   75% 76%   78%

Since the claim that 75% of passengers are satisfied is inside the 95% confidence interval, we do not reject the null hypothesis.

Remember: Unless we have sufficient evidence to the contrary, we do not reject the null hypothesis. We do not challenge H_0. This is **not** the same as saying that we accept the claim.

key point

When working with levels of confidence (or levels of significance), statisticians can use percentages ambiguously. In particular, the 5% level of significance and the 95% level of confidence mean the same thing. That is to say, 5% of the time outside the confidence interval or 95% of the time inside the confidence interval.

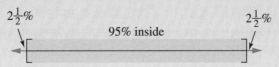

$2\frac{1}{2}\%$ 95% inside $2\frac{1}{2}\%$

exam focus

In the final analysis, testing the null hypothesis H_0 simply involves a confidence interval and a red dot:

Either	Or

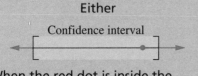

Confidence interval

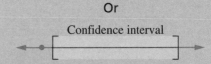

Confidence interval

When the red dot is inside the confidence interval we fail to reject H_0.

When the red dot is outside the confidence interval we reject H_0.

Glossary of Statistical Terms

Arithmetic mean   A measure of central tendency that sums all the scores in the data sets and divides by the number of scores.

Asymptotic   The quality of the normal curve such that the tails never touch the horizontal axis.

Bell-shaped curve (see normal curve)

Bias   Systematic errors in the way the sample represents the population. It can be caused by poorly worded surveys, non-response or undercoverage.

Bivariate data   A survey that examines the relationship between two variables (data sets). In our course, the two variables are usually quantitative variables.

Categorical data   Non-numerical data that can be counted but only described in words. Such data may be ordered or unordered.

Causality   The relationship between an event (the cause) and a second event (the effect).

Class interval   The upper and lower boundary of a set of scores used in the creation of a frequency distribution.

Continuous numerical data   Data which can take any numerical value within a certain range.

Correlation coefficient (r)   A numerical index that reflects the relationship between two variables, constant between -1 and 1.

Data   An item or items of factual information derived from measurement or research.

Data point   An observation.

Data set   A set of data points.

Dependent variable   Often denoted by y, whose value depends on another variable. It is usually represented on the vertical axis.

Direct correlation   A positive correlation where the values of both variables change in the same direction.

Discrete numerical data   Data which can only have certain values.

Frequency distribution   A method for illustrating the distribution of scores within class intervals. Often given in tabular form (frequency distribution table).

Frequency polygon   A graphical representation of a frequency distribution.

Histogram   A graphical representation of a frequency distribution.

Hypothesis   An 'if–then' statement of conjecture that relates variables to one another.

Independent variable   Often denoted by x, whose variation does not depend on another variable. It is usually represented on the horizontal axis.

Inferential statistics   Tools that are used to infer the results based on a sample to a population.

Mean   The value where scores are summed and divided by the number of observations.

Measures of central tendency   The mean, median and mode.

Median   The point at which 50% of the cases in a distribution fall below and 50% fall above.

Mid-interval value   The central value in a class interval.

Mode   The most frequently occurring score in a distribution.

Normal curve   A distribution of scores that is symmetrical about the mean, median and mode and has asymptotic tails.

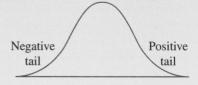

Observed score   The score that is recorded or observed.

Primary data   First-hand data that you collect yourself or are collected by someone under your direct supervision.

Qualitative data   A type of information that describes or characterises, but does not measure, data. Often referred to as non-numerical data.

Quantitative data   A type of information that can be counted or expressed numerically.

Range   The highest value minus the lowest value.

Sample   A subset of a population.

Sampling error   The difference between sample and population values.

Scatter plot   A plot of paired data points.

Secondary data   Second-hand data that have already been collected and made available from an external source such as newspapers, government departments or the internet.

Skew or skewness   The quality of a distribution that defines the disproportionate frequency of certain scores. A longer right tail than left corresponds to a smaller number of occurrences at the high end of the distribution; this is a *positively* skewed distribution. A shorter right tail than left corresponds to a larger number of occurrences at the high end of the distribution; this is a *negatively* skewed distribution.

Standard deviation (σ)   A measure of dispersion (spread) of a set of values from their mean.

Statistics   A set of tools and techniques used to collect, organise, represent and interpret information.

Univariate data   A survey that looks at only one variable (data set). The variable may be either qualitative or quantitative.

Variability   The amount of spread or dispersion in a set of scores.

Variance   The square of the standard deviation, and another measure of a distribution's spread or dispersion.

Calculator Instructions

Casio Natural Display Calculator

Before starting any procedures on the calculator, you should clear the memory.

To clear the memory:

> Shift + 9 : CLR
>
> 3 : All
>
> = : Yes

To perform statistical calculations, we must create a frequency table.

To enter a frequency table, you must switch Frequency on:

> Shift + Mode : Setup
>
> Down Arrow
>
> 3 : STAT
>
> 1 : ON

To enter a table of data:

> Mode
>
> 2 : STAT
>
> 1 : 1-VAR

Enter the data into the table, followed by the = sign each time. Once you have finished entering the data, press the AC button.

To analyse the data in the table:

> Shift + 1 : STAT
>
> 4 : Var

Options are as follows:

$2 : \bar{x}$ (the mean of the terms, also known as μ)

$2 : \sigma x$ (the standard deviation)

key point

For simplicity, to find the mean or standard deviation of a **single list of data**, create a frequency table and set all the frequencies to 1.

Practice exercise

Use your calculator to find the mean and standard deviation of the following table of data:

Value	2	4	6	8	10
Frequency	13	6	9	2	6

The answers are:

Mean $\mu = \bar{x} = 5$ Standard deviation $\sigma x = 2{\cdot}88675$

Sharp WriteView Calculator

Before starting any procedures on the calculator, you should clear the memory.

To clear the memory:

> 2nd F + ALPHA : M-CLR
>> 1 : Memory
>> 0 : Clear

To put the calculator into Statistics mode:

> Mode
>> 1 : STAT
>> 0 : SD

To enter the data:

> Take each value and frequency as a pair of data.
> Enter each value, separated by a comma $(x, 4)$
>> Then press the DATA button
>> (e.g. enter: 2 , 13 DATA)

Once all the pairs of data have been entered, press:

> ON / C

key point

> To find the mean or standard deviation of a **single list of data**, press the DATA button after each value. Leave out the comma and frequency value.

To analyse the data entered:

ALPHA then 4 then $=$: $\bar{x}$ (the mean of the terms, also known as μ)

ALPHA then 6 then $=$: σx (the standard deviation)

Practice exercise

Use your calculator to find the mean and standard deviation of the following table of data:

Value	2	4	6	8	10
Frequency	13	6	9	2	6

The answers are:

> Mean $\mu = \bar{x} = 5$ Standard deviation $\sigma x = 2{\cdot}88675$